I. A. BENCH WOODWORK

JOHN L. FEIRER · Author of
INDUSTRIAL ARTS WOODWORKING
Head, Industrial Education Dept.
Western Michigan University
Kalamazoo, Michigan

Chas. A. Bennett Co., Inc.
Peoria, Illinois

THE PLAN OF THIS BOOK

I. A. BENCH WOODWORK, as a part of a modern industrial-arts program, includes the following as some of its major objectives:

1. It teaches students about the woodworking industry, including sources of lumber, how lumber is made into plywood and other wood materials, how wood projects are designed and produced, and how people earn a living in woodworking. It is a study of one of our most common materials.

2. It teaches the student how to design, plan, and carry through a project in woodworking. He is introduced to the need for planning his own projects and making his own bills of materials for these projects. While most beginning students will not be able to design, they should know how to select well designed projects and make planning sheets, bills of materials, and stock-cutting lists.

3. It teaches basic hand skills in woodworking that are useful to everyone, regardless of the aim in life. Many will use these woodworking skills in their hobbies. Others will find them useful around the home. A small number may use these skills in occupations such as carpentry or teaching of industrial arts.

4. It teaches students how to work safely with woodworking tools and materials, and to protect themselves from accidents.

5. It teaches consumer values. Students learn how to order lumber, plywood, finishing materials, and hardware. They also learn how to select good furniture.

6. It teaches the conservation of natural resources. Students are taught the value of our forests and how they can be preserved.

This book contains 54 units, each of which offers a good learning opportunity. The arrangement of the book makes for great flexibility. Only those units need be covered that meet the outline of a particular course. Questions at the end of each unit focus attention on the important ideas and information.

Over 65 project ideas are found in the text itself and in the project section. If a student needs a detailed drawing, he may choose one from the project section. However, as he grows in his ability to work independently, he may develop his own project drawings, using one of the ideas shown in the text.

This book could be used as a first course in woodwork for any age group, although the illustrations and projects included would probably appeal mostly to early teenages. To make the book more useful to these age groups, *the sentences were checked for length and difficulty*. The *vocabulary* has been confined to the early teenage degree of development. *New words* are defined. *Technical words* and more advanced words have been defined in every case the first time they are used. The sentences are short, to keep the reading level well within the ability of the age group. Older boys should find the book especially easy to follow in a beginning course in woodwork.

An example of simplicity is the spelling of the word "gage". This simpler spelling of "gauge" was used for two reasons. First, modern handbooks and technical publications use the shorter spelling. Second, students often confuse "gauge" with "gouge" and therefore pronounce and use it wrong.

Listed below are the companies that were so generous in cooperating by helping to supply illustrations and other materials. Special assistance was given by those listed in italics.

Adjustable Clamp Company
American Forest Products Industries
American Screw Company
Atlas Press Company
Baker Furniture Company
Behr-Manning Company
Better Light Better Sight Bureau
Boice-Crane Company
Butler Furniture Company

Cincinnati Tool Company (The)
Douglas Fir Plywood Association
Dremel Manufacturing Company
Dunbar Furniture Corporation of Indiana
Franklin Glue Company (The)
General Motors Company
Greenlee Tool Company
H. K. Porter Company
I. P. Hyde Co.
Millers Falls Company
Mummert-Dixon Co.
National Lumber Manufacturing Association
Nicholson File Company
Reynolds Metals Company
Sherwin-Williams Co.
Skil Corporation
Stanley Tools
U. S. Dept. of Agriculture
U. S. Forest Service
U. S. Steel Corporation
Woman's Day (The A & P Magazine)
X-Acto Cresent Products, Inc.
Yates-American Machine Co.

CONTENTS

5

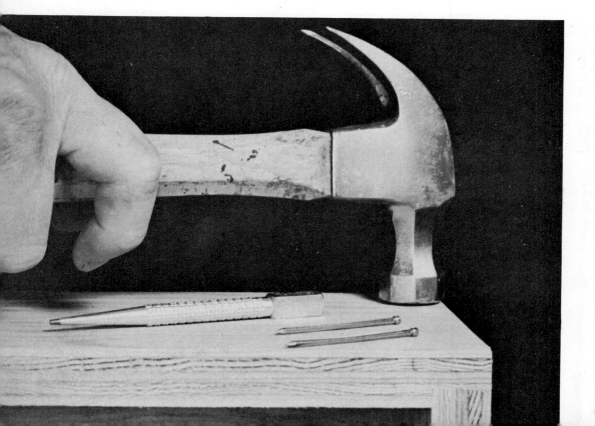

Unit 1. MAKING A PROJECT WITH HAND TOOLS

You will find woodworking both interesting and useful. Fig. 1-1. You'll be making things and working with tools in a shop with others your age. You'll have a chance to use your hands. However, woodworking is more than just "making the chips fly." To do a good job and please yourself, you'll want to learn all you need to know about what you're doing. You'll want to be proud of the project you take home. Whether it's for yourself or a gift for your dad or mother, you'll want it to be the best you can make.

Here are some of the things you'll learn:
• Where wood and other products of trees come from.
• How lumbering is done.
• How plywood and other lumber products are manufactured.
• Common kinds of woods and their uses. Fig. 1-2, page 8.
• How to purchase lumber and other wood supplies.

1-1. It's interesting to make things of wood. Here a group prepares Christmas displays, using thin wood and the jigsaw.

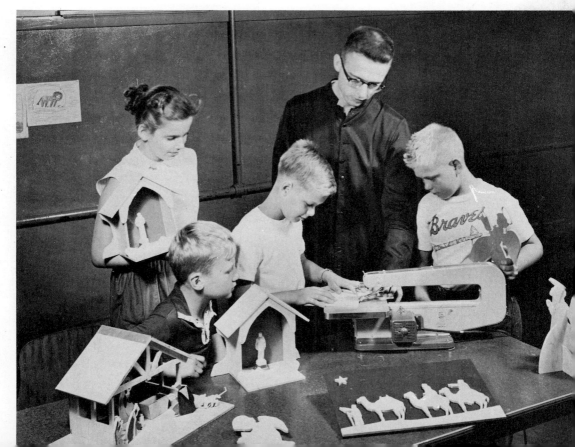

1-2. Learning about lumber is important. Each kind of wood has a "personality" all its own.

• How to purchase wood tools and machines. Fig. 1-3.
• How to work safely with hand tools and simple power tools. Fig. 1-4.
• How to work with others. Fig. 1-5.
• How to design, plan and construct useful and attractive projects. Fig. 1-6.
• How to apply a finish.
• How people earn a living in woodwork.
• How to begin a life-long hobby in woods. Fig. 1-7.
• How to take care of the shop or work area so that it's neat, clean and orderly. Fig. 1-8.

All of these skills and information will come as you make projects with hand tools.

1-3. You'll want to know how to buy good tools for a workshop of your own you'll have some day.

1-4. Getting to know tools makes them your helper.

1-5. Working together in the shop is a good way to learn how to get along with other people.

1-6. You'll really feel pride in a job well done when you've made something of your own in the wood shop.

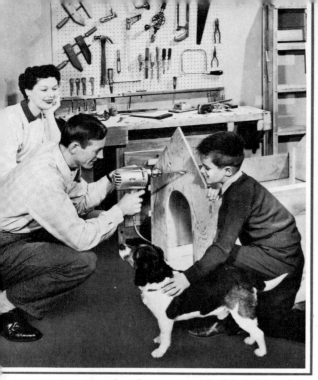

1-7. Woodwork is a wonderful hobby that the whole family can enjoy.

1-8. Do your part in taking care of the shop. One good habit is to return tools to their proper places after using them.

Let's take a look at what you will do when you make a project:

1. Selecting or designing the project. What to make is a big question. Will it be something for yourself or for your room? Will it be a gift for your mother or dad or someone else in your family? Maybe you'd like to make a game or build a piece of sports equipment. Or perhaps you'd like an out-of-doors project for birds or a pet. You, your instructor, and the other students will all help to decide what to make. Sometimes you will find a drawing of the project in a book or magazine. Or maybe you'd like to design your own project. Your instructor may want you to build the first project from a design he has chosen. The students in the class may decide to vote on what will be the second project. After you've learned some of the basic skills, you will probably select and design a project all your own. Let's suppose you've decided to make the note box shown in Fig. 1-9.

1-9. Here's a note box that might be a good beginning project.

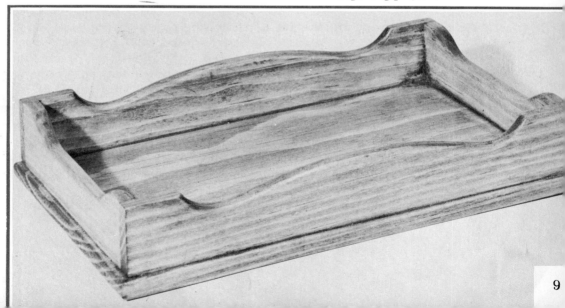

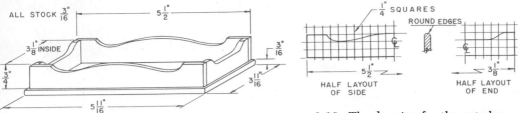

ALL STOCK 3/16"

3 1/8" INSIDE

5 1/2"

3/16"

3 11/16"

5 11/16"

1/4" SQUARES

ROUND EDGES

5 1/2"

HALF LAYOUT
OF SIDE

3 1/8"

HALF LAYOUT
OF END

1-10. The drawing for the note box.

1-11. The planning sheet.

PLANNING SHEET

Name _____ Grade _____

Note Box

| Name of the Project | Date Started | Date Completed |

BILL OF MATERIALS:

No.	T	W	L	Name of Part	Material	Unit Cost	Total Cost
1	3/16"	3 11/16"	5 11/16"	Bottom	Pine		
2	3/16"	3/4"	5 1/2"	Sides	Pine		
2	3/16"	3/4"	3 1/8"	Ends	Pine		

TOOLS AND MACHINES:

Rule, try square, crosscut and rip saw, jack plane, file, coping or jig saw, hammer, sandpaper and pencil.

Procedures or Steps:

1. Cut stock for each part to rough size.
2. Square up bottom to correct size.
3. Square up sides and ends.
4. Transfer design to the sides and ends.
5. Cut sides and ends to shape with coping or jig saw.
6. Round all edges of the bottom and upper edges of the sides and ends.
7. Sand all pieces smooth.
8. Put sides and ends together with glue and brads.
9. Attach bottom to sides and ends with glue and brads.
10. Apply the desired finish.

2. Reading a drawing and making a sketch. You must be able to read a drawing to find the answers to these questions: Fig. 1-10.

• What is the overall size of the bottom?
• How big are the sides? The ends?
• Are the sides and ends the same shape?

Sometimes it will be necessary to make a *shop sketch* to keep with you all the time you're building the project. A shop sketch is always needed when you design your own project. It's also needed if the project is in a magazine or book in the library that you can't keep.

3. Selecting the materials. What materials will you use to make the note box? Will it be pine, cedar or poplar? Could plywood be used? How would you buy it if you had to go to a lumber yard yourself?

4. Planning your work (see Unit 5).

What is the size of each part of the box? How many parts are alike? Fig. 1-11 shows you the complete bill of materials for this box. How will you make it? What steps will you follow? What tools will you need? Fig. 1-11 shows how the plan of procedure or planning sheet for this project will look after it is complete. Notice what must be done before you are ready to use tools. Sure, you can start to make this box without plans. But will you know what you are doing? Chances are you won't be satisfied with it after it is finished.

5. Building the project. Now you are ready to follow steps described in this book.

6. Rating the project. After the project is finished, ask yourself these questions: Am I satisfied with it? Will I do better the next time? How can I improve on the next project?

QUESTIONS

1. List some of the things you should learn in woodworking.
2. How is a first project in woodworking usually chosen?
3. Why must you be able to read a drawing?
4. Would you know how to buy lumber at a lumber yard?
5. What is a bill of materials?
6. Why should you rate the project after building it?

Unit 2. SAFETY IN THE WOOD SHOP

This is a true-life story: It was Friday afternoon in the wood shop and Jim was to pitch for his baseball team the next day. But he was anxious to finish the baseball equipment rack he was building for his room. He needed to use a chisel to trim a board. His teacher had warned him to keep his hands away from the sharp edge of the chisel, but Jim was in a hurry and thought he didn't have time to clamp the work in a vise. He held the wood in one hand and used the other hand to operate the chisel. Things were going along fine. Then the chisel slipped and the cutting edge hit Jim's thumb, cutting a deep gash. The school nurse put a bandage on it and told him he couldn't use the hand for several days. This meant no game and a painful cut besides. If only he'd followed the rules! Jim was lucky, though. The accident could have been a lot worse. If he had been working on a machine, he might have lost a finger.

What was wrong? For one thing, Jim wasn't following good safety habits. He failed to practice two important lessons: First, that he must always follow directions. Second, that he must never take chances. You must *never* take chances in the shop. Always read the instructions in this book for each step, and watch your instructor as he demonstrates. Of course, everything you do has some danger to it; you can get hurt playing a game as well as working in a shop. To keep yourself safe, you must learn the hazards and avoid them by following good safety practices.

Here are some rules you must observe in the wood shop:

1. Always dress correctly for the job.
• Roll up your sleeves and tuck in your tie or remove it. Fig. 2-1. Never wear loose-fitting clothes.
• The standard dress in the shop is a protective apron. Wear one.
• Always wear eye shields or goggles

2-1. This is the way to dress for work. When carrying tools, be sure the points or cutting edges are held downward.

2-3. Keep oily rags and waste in metal cans. An oily rag can start a fire by itself.

when grinding, sanding, or drilling. Fig. 2-2.

• Remove rings and other jewelry when using power tools.

2. Follow directions.

• The correct way is the safe way. The safe way is shown in this book.

• Your instructor will show you how to do things correctly and safely.

• Never try to get by "just this once." That's usually the time an accident happens.

• A good slogan to follow is, "It is better to be safe than sorry." The A, B, C's of safety are Always Be Careful.

3. Do your share in good shop housekeeping.

• Keep the top of your bench and the floor around it clean and neat.

• Put your tools away after you have used them.

• When carrying tools, always keep the pointed ends down and away from you.

• Wipe up oil and grease spots. Keep rags in a metal container. Fig. 2-3.

• Place scrap stock in scrap boxes immediately.

• *Don't "wait for George" to do it.* A clean shop is a safer shop.

4. Learn to use tools correctly.

• A cutting tool must have a sharp edge to do a good job. A sharp tool cuts the wood easily. A dull tool could slip and cut you.

• Never try to test the sharpness of tools on your hand or fingers. Always use wood or paper.

• Keep your hands away from the front of sharp-edged cutting tools.

• Be especially careful when you use your finger or hand as a guide when starting a cutting tool.

2-2. You have only one pair of eyes. You can't buy a new pair. *Protect them.*

2-4. Tools will soon become dull or broken if you handle them like this. Never carry more tools than you can handle easily.

2-5. If this chisel could talk it would say, "Ouch, you're ruining my cutting edge. I'll never be able to do good work again."

2-6. The school shop isn't a playground. Always remember that it is dangerous to fool around a shop. Somebody could get hurt.

• Make sure that your tools are in good condition. Check to see that the handles are not broken or cracked and that they are fastened tightly. Fig. 2-4.
• Remember to use the correct tool for the job every time. Don't misuse tools. For example, don't use a chisel to open a wooden box or a can of paint. Fig. 2-5.

5. Avoid horseplay. This is the most dangerous thing you can do. Fig. 2-6. Practical jokes in the shop aren't funny. Fig. 2-7. Would you like to cause a friend's accident? Wrestling, pushing, shoving, or tripping usually end in an accident. Your instructor can't allow it and *you can't afford it.*

6. Report every accident no matter how small. Get first aid for every cut or scratch. An infection can start from even the smallest cut. Always get help from someone who knows how to remove something from your eye.

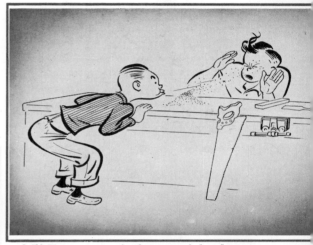

2-7. Keep practical jokes out of the shop.

QUESTIONS

1. What happened to Jim on a certain "Black Friday" afternoon?

2. Tell how to dress correctly in the wood shop.

3. Why is it important to follow directions?

4. Name some things you should do to help keep the shop in good order.

5. Why is it important to learn how to use tools correctly?

6. What is the most dangerous thing you can do in a shop?

7. Why is it important to report all accidents?

SAFETY

Unit 3. ORDERING LUMBER, PLYWOOD, AND OTHER WOOD PRODUCTS

You don't have to be an expert to start making something in the shop. As you work with woods, you'll learn more and more about the lumber you're using. One thing is learning how to buy lumber in a lumber yard. This will save you money. Lumber is expensive and you won't want to waste it. Here are some things you should know:

1. What lumber is. Lumber comes from trees, and we call it wood. Fig.

3-1. *Wood* is the hard substance under the bark of trees and shrubs. If you could look at a piece of wood through a microscope, you would see that it is made up of long, narrow tubes. Each tube is as small as a hair on your head. These tubes, or wood fibers, usually grow straight up and down. This makes wood straight-grained. You can see from looking at Fig. 3-2 that it is easier to cut with the grain than across it. When you cut across the grain, you must cut through the packed fibers.

The tree trunk is cut lengthwise into lumber. Some of the fibers are cut off at an angle. This makes the grain surface look something like Fig. 3-3.

2. How lumber is classified. Lumber is classified either as softwood or hard-

3-1. Parts of a tree.

3-2. It's easy to see why wood can be cut with the grain easier than across it. This shows the tube structure of wood.

CROWN

Trees increase each year in height and spread of branches by adding a new growth of twigs. This new growth comes from young cells in the buds at the ends of the twigs.

TRUNK

The tree trunk supports the crown and produces the bulk of the useful wood.

ROOTS

Roots anchor the tree; absorb water, dissolved minerals and nitrogen necessary for the living cells which make the food; and help hold the soil against erosion. A layer of growth cells at the root tips makes new root tissue throughout the growing season.

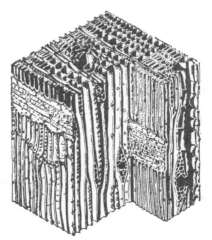

3-3. The surface of lumber looks like this when it is cut.

SOFT WOOD
(Conifers)

PINE

3-4. Softwoods are used in house construction and for some of the small articles you will make.

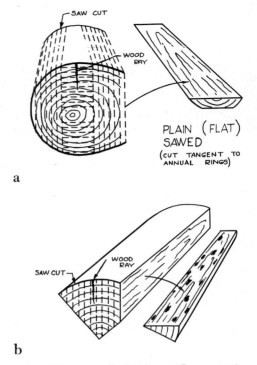

SAW CUT

WOOD RAY

PLAIN (FLAT) SAWED
(CUT TANGENT TO ANNUAL RINGS)

a

WOOD RAY

SAW CUT

b

3-6. (a) Plain-sawed lumber (flat grain). (b) Quarter-sawed lumber (edge grain).

wood. *Softwoods* come from evergreen, or needle-bearing, trees. Fig. 3-4. Common softwoods are pine, cedar, fir, and redwood. *Hardwoods* come from broad-leafed trees that shed their leaves in the fall. Fig. 3-5. Some of these are birch, maple, oak, walnut, cherry, poplar, and mahogany. You

3-5. Hardwoods are used for furniture and trim.

HARD WOOD
(Broad-Leaved)

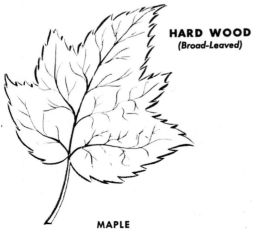

MAPLE

will soon find that these terms don't tell how hard the wood really is. Some softwoods are actually harder than some hardwoods! Hardwoods usually (but not always) cost more than softwoods. See Unit 52.

3. How boards are cut from logs. Boards are cut from logs in two major ways. The cheapest and most economical way is called *plain-sawed* (when it is a hardwood tree) or *flat-grained* (when it is a softwood tree). The log is squared and sawed lengthwise from one side to the other. *Quarter-sawed* (for hardwood) or *edge-grained* (for softwood) is a more expensive method of cutting. It shows a better grain pattern especially in oak and other hardwoods. Fig. 3-6b.

4. How lumber is worked. Some lumber is purchased just as it comes from the saw mills. The surface of the

15

Standard Sizes of Softwoods		Standard Thickness of Hardwoods	
Stock Size	Actual Size	Rough	S2S
1″ x 2″	¾″ x 1⅝″	⅜″	3⁄16″
1″ x 3″	¾″ x 2⅝″	½″	5⁄16″
1″ x 4″	¾″ x 3⅝″	⅝″	7⁄16″
1″ x 8″	¾″ x 7½″	¾″	9⁄16″
1″ x 10″	¾″ x 9½″	1″	13⁄16″
2″ x 2″	1⅝″ x 1⅝″	1¼″	1 1⁄16″
2″ x 4″	1⅝″ x 3⅝″		
2″ x 6″	1⅝″ x 5⅝″		
2″ x 10″	1⅝″ x 9½″		
4″ x 4″	3⅝″ x 3⅝″		

3-7. This table shows the common sizes of softwood and hardwood in both their rough and actual sizes.

lumber is rough "Rgh". It must be smoothed by running it through a machine called a surfacer, or planer, before it can be used in the shop. Most lumber comes from the lumber yard already smoothed (surfaced, or dressed). Lumber can be purchased surfaced on two sides (S2S), or surfaced on four sides (S4S). You would purchase surfaced, or dressed, lumber if you wanted to build something at home.

5. How to understand lumber sizes. When you buy a piece of 2-by-4 lumber (2 inches by 4 inches), you'll find that it doesn't measure exactly that much. Its actual size is 1 ⅝ inches by 3 ⅝ inches. The rough size board was larger than that but became smaller when it was seasoned and surfaced. This is true of all surfaced lumber. The actual size of a surfaced 1-inch board is 13/16 inch. In Fig. 3-7, the rough and finished sizes for softwoods and hardwoods are shown.

6. How lumber is dried. When the tree is first cut down all wood is green and contains a lot of moisture. The logs are cut into boards which are placed in the open air to dry. Lumber dried in this way is called *air-dried lumber*

(AD). It retains about 12 to 15 per cent moisture. A better way to dry the lumber is in special drying rooms called kilns (pronounced "kills"). *Kiln-dried lumber* (KD) has only about 6 to 12 per cent moisture. This is the kind to buy for fine projects and furniture.

7. How softwood lumber is graded. The *select*, or best, grades of softwood lumber are *Grade A and Grade B*. These are often sold as "B and better." B-and-better lumber is used for trim on the inside of a house and for projects you make in the school shop. *C and D grades* of lumber are less expensive but can be used for the same things as *Grades A and B*. *Common lumber* is used only for rough purposes such as in house framing.

8. How hardwoods are graded. The best grade of hardwood is *FAS*. This means "firsts and seconds." It is the best grade for making furniture. *Number 1* and *number 2* have some defects and are poorer quality than FAS.

9. How lumber is sold. A *board foot* of lumber is a piece 1 inch thick, 12 inches wide, and 1 foot (12 inches) long. The board foot is the standard unit of measurement used in lumber yards. Lumber less than 1 inch thick is figured as 1 inch. This is a way to figure board feet: multiply the thickness in inches by the width in feet by the length in feet. For example, a 2 by 4 inch piece that is 12 feet long would be 8 board feet: $2 \times 4/12 \times 12 = 8$. The width (4 inches) is divided by 12 to change it to feet.

A simpler way to figure board feet for small projects is as follows: Board feet equals the thickness in inches times the width in inches times the length in feet over 12. Board Feet (BF) =

$$\frac{T \text{ (in inches)} \times W \text{ (in inches)} \times L \text{ (in feet)}}{12}$$

For example: How many board feet are there in a piece of white pine 1 inch by 7 inches by 6 feet?

$$BF = \frac{1 \times 7 \times 6}{12}, \text{ or } 3\frac{1}{2} \text{ board feet.}$$

For very small pieces found in many smaller projects, you can figure board feet this way: Board feet equals the thickness in inches times the width in inches times the length in inches divided by 144. There are 144 cubic inches in one board foot.

$$\text{Board Feet (BF)} = \frac{T \times W \times L \text{ (all in inches)}}{144}$$

For example: How many board feet are there in a piece of walnut $\frac{1}{2}$ inch thick, 9 inches wide and 28 inches long? (Remember that stock less than 1 inch thick is figured as 1 inch).

$$BF = \frac{1 \times 9 \times 28}{144} \text{ or } 1\frac{3}{4} \text{ board feet.}$$

Lumber is sold by the board foot, by the hundred board feet, or by the thousand board feet (M). For example, if lumber sells for $350.00 per M, if would cost you $35.00 for 100 board feet and 35 cents for one board foot. If you purchased one board foot, the piece would be about 3/4 to 13/16 inch thick, 11½ to 11⅝ inches wide, and 12 inches long.

10. How to order lumber. To order lumber you must specify:

- The number of pieces you want.
- The size of the pieces.
- The kind of wood.
- The grade of lumber.
- The surface (whether it is rough or surfaced).
- Whether it is air-dried or kiln-dried.

11. How plywood is purchased. *Plywood* is made by gluing several layers of thin wood together. The outside plies are called faces. The center ply or plies make up the core. The core may be one or more layers of *veneer* (thin sheets of wood) or solid lumber.

The grain of the plies is placed at right angles to each other. There are usually three, five, seven, or nine plies (layers). For example, ¼-inch plywood may have either three or five plies. Of course, the more plys there are, the stiffer the plywood is. Interior fir plywood is used for projects that are painted or enameled. On hardwood plywoods, the outside ply (called the veneer, or face) is a layer of good hardwood such as birch, mahogany, walnut, cherry, or gum. There are two ways or systems of grading plywood. Plywood that has a softwood layer on both sides is called *good two sides,* or *A-A.* This is the best fir plywood. Custom, or good, grade hardwood plywood is best for furniture projects. Plywood comes in standard thickness such as ¼, ⅜, ½ inch, etc. The most common size of plywood sheet is 4 feet by 8 feet. However, you can buy smaller or larger sheets. For example, for small projects, a 4-feet-by-4-feet panel is very convenient. Plywood is sold by the square foot. A piece 2 feet wide and 4 feet long has 8 square feet.

12. Other wood materials. *Hardboard* consists mostly of wood fibers held together with bonding material (glue). The wood fibers are treated with chemicals and then pressed together under thousands of pounds of pressure. There are two types of hardboard; *standard,* or *untreated,* and *tempered,* or *treated.* In the tempering process the pressed boards are dipped in drying oils and baked in an oven. This increases the strength of the board. One face (surface) of the hardboard is very smooth, while the other is rough and looks like screening. Hardboard can be used for many things such as parts of furniture and home construction. One kind of tempered hardboard has holes all over the surface. This can be used for hanger boards for such things as tools and class displays. The standard sizes are ⅛ inch by 4 feet by 6 feet, and ¼ inch by 4 feet by 12 feet. *Fiberboard* is a softer building board made from pressed wood and other vegetable fibers. It is used for bulletin boards and for many building uses. It is made 1/8 inch and 3/16 inch thick in sheets 4 feet by 6 feet and in 4-by-8-foot sheets in ¼-inch and ⅜-inch thicknesses.

QUESTIONS

1. What is lumber?
2. Name the parts of a tree.
3. What is the difference between softwood and hardwood?
4. Name two ways of cutting a log.
5. What does S2S mean?
6. What is the actual size of a 2 by 4?
7. Name two ways of drying lumber.
8. What is the best grade of select lumber?
9. What are common lumbers used for?
10. What is the best grade of hardwood lumber?
11. What is a board foot?
12 How many board feet are there in a piece 1 inch by 10 inches by 8 feet?
13. What information should be included to order lumber correctly?
14. What is plywood?
15. What are the common thicknesses of plywood?
16. How is plywood sold?
17. What is hardboard?
18. Tell how hardboard is made.
19. Describe fiberboard.

Unit 4. READING A DRAWING AND MAKING A SHOP SKETCH

Before you can build a project, you must have a drawing or blueprint of it. Fig. 4-1. This drawing will tell you how big each part is, what the material is, what shape each part is, and how the parts go together. When you make your own design, it shows how the finished article will look, so there is no guessing to do. Before you can use a drawing, though, you'll have to know how to read it. The drawing is your guide. It tells you everything you need to know about the project.

4-2. A three-view drawing of a book end.

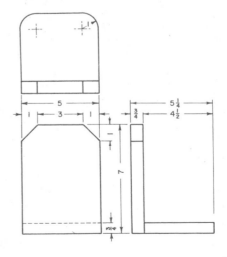

4-1. Learn to follow a drawing as you build your project.

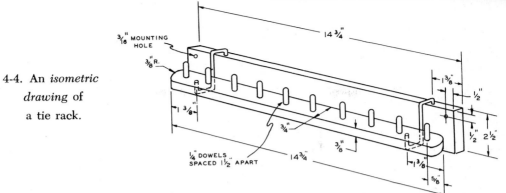

4-4. An *isometric drawing* of a tie rack.

4-3. Only two views of this wall shelf are shown. The pictorial drawing shows how the shelf will look when it is finished.

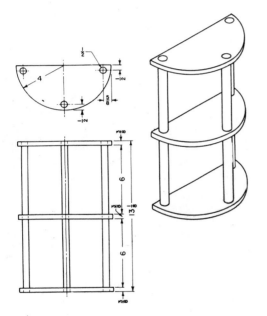

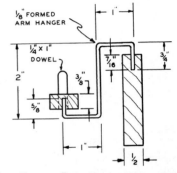

angle) and *cabinet* drawings. Fig. 4-4 and Fig. 4-5. Notice that both of these

4-5. A *cabinet drawing* of a pipe rack.

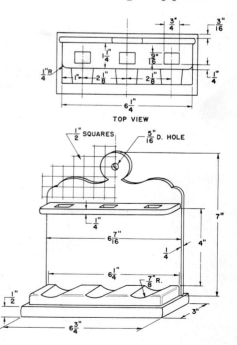

TOP VIEW

If you've already taken drawing and sketching, the following will be a review.

DRAWINGS USED IN WOODWORKING. As you look through this book, you'll see that most drawings are *working*, or *view, drawings*. These have two or more views (usually three) of the project. Fig. 4-2 and 4-3. The most common views are the *front, top* and *right side*, or *end*. Many drawings found in magazines are pictorial drawings. The two most common are *isometric* (equal-

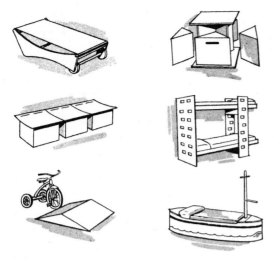

4-6. Perspective sketches of some wood projects.

drawings show how the project will look when it is completed and the size and shape of each part. Sometimes even a *perspective* drawing is used. Fig. 4-6. Woodworking drawings differ. A drawing of a project will often be made partly as a view drawing and partly as a pictorial drawing. Then, too, when view drawings are used, the views are not always placed correctly. That is, the right side, or end, view isn't always to the right of the front view. You'll also find many drawings made as *exploded* (taken apart) views.

4-7. The meaning of lines.

Border line - very heavy

Visible outline, or object line - heavy

Invisible or hidden line

Center line

Extension line

Dimension line

This kind shows each part more clearly and also how the parts fit together.

WHAT LINES MEAN. Lines show the shape of each part. Fig. 4-7. Here's what they mean:

1. Visible, or **outline, lines** show all edges or surfaces that can be seen.

2. Hidden, or **invisible, lines** show hidden edges.

3. Center lines are used to show the centers of arcs and circles and to divide an object into symmetrical (equal) parts.

4. Extension lines stick out from the drawing. Between these lines the sizes of each part can be shown.

5. Dimension lines usually have arrowheads at one or both ends and are broken in the center. They show the dimensions, or sizes, of *each part* and of the *whole object.*

DIMENSIONS. *Dimensions* tell the sizes. These dimensions must be followed in making a bill of materials and in constructing each part. Most woodworking drawings are dimensioned in inches and fractions (parts) of an inch. Sometimes the inch mark (") is placed after the dimension to show that the size is given in inches. All project dimensions in this book are in inches, whether the inch mark is used or not.

SCALE. Nearly always a woodworking project is too big to be drawn full size on a piece of paper. Very large projects must be made to a smaller *scale* so they can be drawn on standard-size paper. Drawings made larger or smaller than full size are called *scale drawings.* For example, if the part is 8 inches long and you draw it 4 inches long, you are using a scale that is *half size,* (6 inches equals 1 foot). Other common scales are: *one-fourth size,* or 3 inches equals 1 foot; and *one-eighth size,* or 1½ inches equal 1 foot.

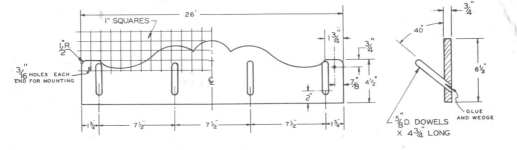

4-8. Can you answer the questions by reading this drawing?

Remember that dimensions tell the size of each part. Object lines show the *shape* of an object.

READING A DRAWING. In Fig. 4-8, you see the kind of project you might make in the wood shop. Find the answers to these questions by reading the drawing:

• How many parts are there in this project? (Count the dowels, too.)
• What is the thickness of the back?
• What is the length of the back?
• What is the diameter of the dowels?
• At what angle are the dowels attached to the back?
• What is the diameter of the holes for mounting the rack?
• How far in are the dowels placed from the ends?
• What is the distance between the dowels?

MAKING A SHOP SKETCH. A *shop sketch* is just a very simple drawing of a project made on ruled drawing paper. Sometimes you'll find an idea you want to use in a book or magazine in the library. Or perhaps you'll find a suggestion in your own book that you like but want to change a little. You might want to use an idea of your own. or sketch something you have seen. You'll need to get this idea "on paper" so you can see what it will look like. Here again a shop sketch is necessary. Regardless of where the idea comes from, you need a shop sketch for planning and building anything.

For making the shop sketch, you need the following materials.
• A No. 2 *writing* pencil or an HB *drawing pencil*.
• *Squared or cross-sectioned paper* that is lined in squares or dots, eight to the inch. These squares or dots help you to draw the plan to the correct size and to keep your lines straight.
• A *pencil compass* may be used for drawing circles and arcs (parts of circles). However, you can sketch these freehand (with no instruments, just a pencil).
• A *shop rule* or a *straightedge* for drawing straight lines.

Here's how to make a shop sketch:

1. Decide on the views you'll need to build the project. Sometimes one view is enough. For example, if it's a one-piece project, such as a cutting board, only the outline view is needed. A little note on the sketch can tell you the thickness of the *stock* (wood). At other times, you'll have to make two or three views.

2. Decide on the scale to use. Make the drawing full size, if possible, in your first attempt, because this is simplest. Maybe you'll need to use more than one piece of cross-sectioned paper to do this. But for all needs, with paper having eight squares to the inch, the following scales are easiest:

21

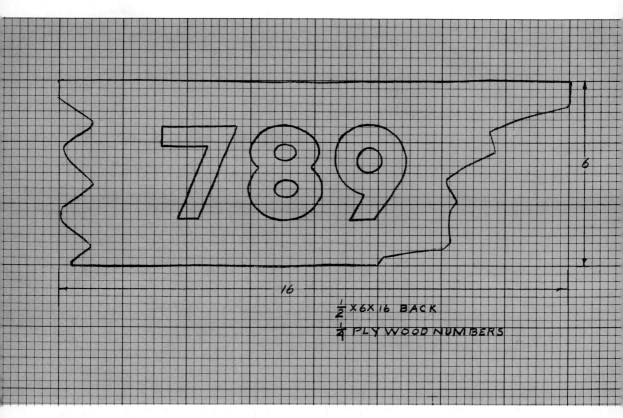

4-9. A shop sketch of house numbers.

• *Full size:* each small square represents (stands for) 1/8 inch and so each large, dark-lined square represents 1 inch.
• *Half size:* each small square represents 1/4 inch and each large square equals 2 inches.
• *Quarter size:* each small square represents 1/2 inch and each large square equals 4 inches.
• *Eighth size:* each small square represents 1 inch and each large square represents 8 inches.

For example, suppose you want to draw the house numbers shown in Fig. 4-9. Notice that the back is 6 inches wide and 16 inches long. You couldn't make this full size, so half size would be best. Always make the drawing as large as possible. Each square in this case will represent 1/4 inch.

3. Start in the lower lefthand corner of the paper about 1 inch up and 1 inch in. Mark a dot.

4. Count off eight large squares to the left. (Each large square equals 2 inches.) Mark a dot.

5. Count off three large squares up. Mark a dot.

6. Notice that the ends are irregular. Mark off three large squares from the lower righthand corner. Draw any free (irregular) line to the upper righthand corner. Draw an irregular line on the other end.

7. Then draw the lines to complete the outline.

8. Now draw in the numbers of your house.

9. Add a note for the size of stock.

1. What are the three views usually shown in a working drawing?
2. Name three kinds of pictorial drawings.
3. What are dimensions?
4. Why do you need dimensions on a drawing?
5. What is a scale drawing?
6. Tell how to make a shop sketch.

Unit 5. PLANNING YOUR WORK

What are you going to do next summer? Is your family going to take a trip? Will you work for your dad or some of your neighbors? Are you going to camp? Will you go to the beach or the mountains? If your summer is to be successful, whether it's work or play, you have to make plans. Before you can do anything that is interesting and worthwhile, you have to get ready for it. Nothing takes care of itself.

In the workaday world where men are paid for their ideas and efforts, planning is a most important part of the job. The engineer is a planner. Without his planning, there wouldn't be much of a chance of building bridges, roads, or large office buildings. The industrial designer, too, spends much of his time planning new products, new ways of getting jobs done, and how to build things. We would be lost without men who can plan.

Plans must be made not only for the big things like buildings but also for small things. You couldn't even play a game of touch or flag football without plans. Planning is especially important when you are going to use tools and materials to make things. In fact, the job is already half done when it is well planned. A good slogan to follow is "Plan your work; then work your plan". Sure, you can start right out "butchering wood." But if you do, you'll waste a lot of lumber (and lum-ber costs money), do poor work, and end up with something nobody wants.

How do you plan in wood? Suppose all of you in the class and your instructor have decided on the first project. In making your plans, you will need the following:

YOU WILL NEED:

1. A drawing of the project or a shop sketch that you have made yourself. This drawing or sketch must have the dimensions on it.

2. A *bill of materials.* This is a list of all the things you will need to build the project. Always make out this bill of materials before you start because:
• It tells you exactly what size and kind of lumber and plywood you need.
• It helps you find out how much the project will cost.
• It makes a good list to take with you if you must buy your own materials.
• It is a good check list to use when you are getting the materials together in the shop.

A complete bill of materials includes *everything* you need to build the project. Notice that this list includes:
• Number of pieces needed.
• Thickness, width, and length of each piece.
• Name of each part.
• Kind of lumber or plywood.
• Cost.

Name _____ Grade _____

Note Holder
_____

| Name of the Project | Date Started | Date Completed |

Bill of Materials:

No.	T	W	L	Name of Part	Material	Unit Cost	Total Cost
1	$\frac{1}{2}''$	$3''$	$7''$	Front	Pine		
1	$\frac{1}{2}''$	$2\frac{3}{4}''$	$4\frac{1}{2}''$	Base	Pine		
1	$\frac{1}{8}''$	$2\frac{3}{4}''$	$4\frac{1}{2}''$	Back	Pine		
1	$\frac{5}{8}''$	$\frac{5}{8}''$	$\frac{5}{8}''$	Pencil top	Pine		

TOOLS AND MACHINES:

Crosscut saw, coping or jig saw, back saw, rule, try square, pencil, jack plane, twist drill, hand drill, sandpaper, drill press, hammer, screw driver.

PROCEDURES OR STEPS:

1. Make a stock-cutting list.
2. Layout and cut all pieces to size.
3. Complete the front.
   - Enlarge the design.
   - Transfer the design to the wood.
   - Cut out design with coping or jig saw.
   - Smooth the edges.
   - Drill the holes for the pencil.
4. Square up the base.
5. Lay out and cut the back to shape.
6. Assemble the parts with screws and nails.
7. Make the ball for the end of the pencil.
8. Apply the finish.

5-1. A planning sheet.

The *size* of each part listed in the bill of materials is the *exact dimension.* But before you get out your materials, you can make a *stock-cutting list.* This is the size of each piece that you cut out of the lumber, before the finished size. To the sizes in the bill of materials you must add about 1/16 to ⅛ inch for thickness, ⅛ to ¼ inch for width, and ½ inch for length. (Of course, plywood is cut from the exact thickness and as close to finished size as possible. See Unit 3.)

3. A list of the steps that you will follow in making each part, putting the project together, and applying a finish. Each unit in this book describes a step in making a project.

4. A list of the hand tools you will use and any power machines you will be allowed to operate.

To help with your planning, use the form shown in Fig. 5-1. Fill out the form as carefully as you can. Check it. Did you forget anything? When your plan is approved, you can begin to draw the project. Check off each step as you do it. Fig. 5-2.

In this first planning, follow the example shown in Fig. 5-1. Notice that (1) there is a clear, easy-to-read drawing, (2) the bill of materials tells exactly what you need, (3) the steps in making the project are easy to follow, and (4) the list of tools includes only those really needed.

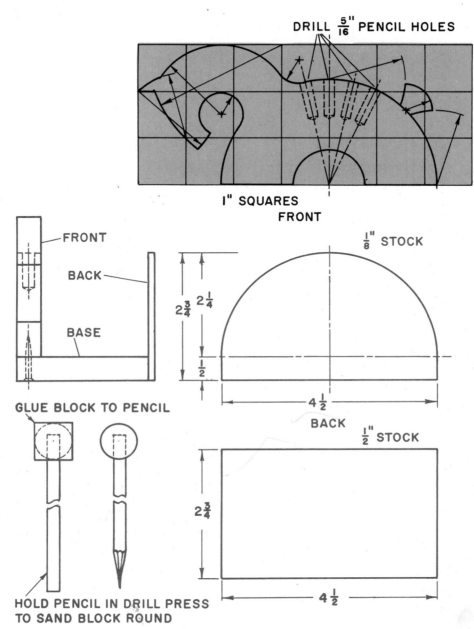

DRILL $\frac{5}{16}''$ PENCIL HOLES

1" SQUARES
FRONT

FRONT

BACK

BASE

GLUE BLOCK TO PENCIL

$\frac{1}{8}''$ STOCK

$2\frac{3}{4}$ $2\frac{1}{4}$

$\frac{1}{2}$

$4\frac{1}{2}$

BACK
$\frac{1}{2}''$ STOCK

$2\frac{3}{4}$

$4\frac{1}{2}$

HOLD PENCIL IN DRILL PRESS
TO SAND BLOCK ROUND

5-2. Drawing for a note holder.

QUESTIONS

1. Why is it important to plan your work?
2. What kind of projects could you plan to make in an industrial-arts wood shop?
3. Name the four important parts of a plan. Describe each one.

4. Is a cutting list the same as a bill of materials?
5. How can a plan help you do your work faster and better?
6. What could happen if you failed to plan your work? List some of the mistakes you could make.

25

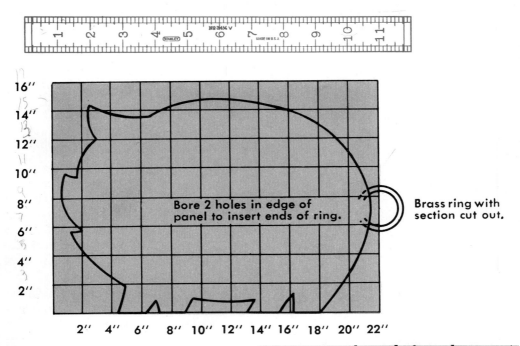

16''
14''
12''
10''
8''   Bore 2 holes in edge of   Brass ring with
6''   panel to insert ends of ring. section cut out.
4''
2''

2'' 4'' 6'' 8'' 10'' 12'' 14'' 16'' 18'' 20'' 22''

6-1. If the thickness of this stock is 1 inch, what size lumber would be needed to make this cutting board?

How wide is the printing on this page? What size stock do you need to make the cutting board shown in Fig. 6-1? You can find these answers only if you know how to measure. That means you must be able to read a rule. Your first work steps include (1) measuring to see if the wood is large enough and (2) marking out the amount you need for each piece.

RULES.

1. A *bench rule* is a wood rule with brass tips on the ends. One side is graduated (divided) in eighths of an inch on both edges. The other side is graduated in sixteenths. Fig. 6-2. The brass

6-2. Bench rule. (Stanley Tools)

tips protect the ends from damage. A damaged rule doesn't measure accurately. Bench rules are made in 1-foot (12 inches), 2-foot (24 inches), and 3-foot (36 inches) lengths. Sometimes the 3-foot rule is called a *yardstick*, which is marked in *feet, inches,* and *parts of an inch.* The inch is divided into *halves, quarters, eighths,* and *sixteenths.* Fig. 6-3.

2. The *zigzag rule* is used to measure longer stock when very exact measurements are not too important. Fig. 6-4. This rule, when open, is usually 6 or 8 feet long.

3. The *push-pull, steel tape,* or *tape*

6-3. Parts of an inch.

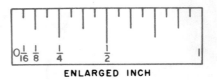

ENLARGED INCH

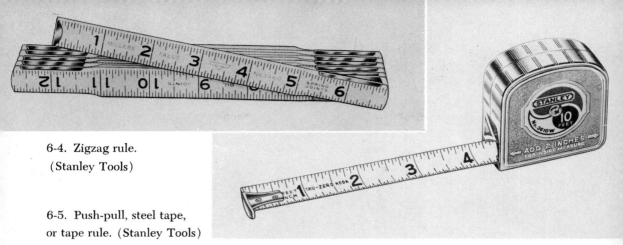

6-4. Zigzag rule.
(Stanley Tools)

6-5. Push-pull, steel tape,
or tape rule. (Stanley Tools)

rule is a very compact metal rule that comes in lengths of 6, 8, or 10 feet. Fig. 6-5. There is a hook at the end to slip over the edge of the board. Since it is flexible (bends easily) it can measure curved surfaces. It is also very good for measuring the inside of things.

SQUARES

1. The *try square* is used for squaring, measuring and testing. Fig. 6-6. The *blade and handle* are at right angles (90 degrees) to each other. It is used (a) to test if a surface is level, (b) to check a face and edge surface for squareness and, (c) to mark lines across the face or edge of stock. There are graduations along the edge of the rule for measuring. *Never use this tool for pounding or hammering.*

2. The *combination square* is being used more and more by woodworkers because it can do so many things. Fig. 6-7. It has a blade and a head. The

6-6. Parts of a try square. (Stanley Tools)

6-7. Parts of a combination square. (Stanley Tools)

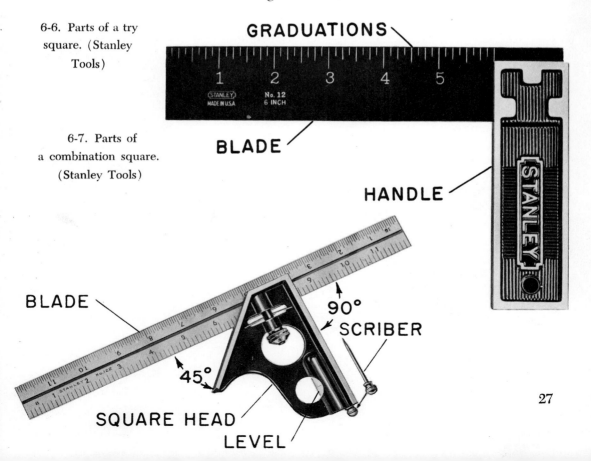

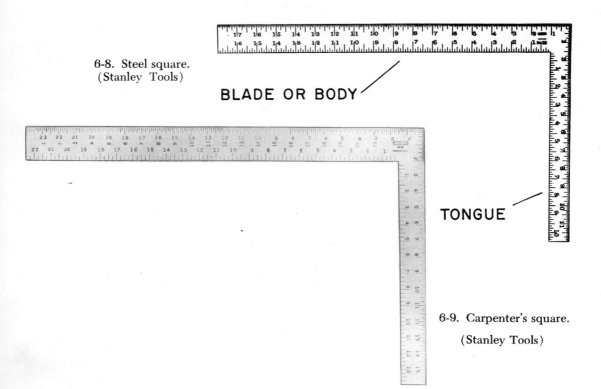

6-8. Steel square.
(Stanley Tools)

BLADE OR BODY

TONGUE

6-9. Carpenter's square.

(Stanley Tools)

blade has a groove cut along its length so it can slide into the head. One side of the head makes a 90-degree angle with the blade and the other side a 45-degree angle. There is a *level* (a tool for testing for a flat, horizontal surface) in the handle. It can be used (a) as a *try square*, (b) as a *miter square* to lay out 45-degree angles and check them, (c) as a *depth gage*, (d) as a *level*, and (e) as a *marking gage*.

3. The *steel square* is a single-thickness metal square. The body varies in length from 12 to 18 inches and the tongue from 8 to 12 inches. Fig. 6-8.

4. The *carpenter's square* (also called a *framing square*) is a large steel square used for measuring and

layout. The body is 2 by 24 inches and the tongue is 1½ by 16 inches. There are tables of figures on this to help the carpenter while working on a house. Fig. 6-9.

MARKING TOOLS

1. An ordinary *lead pencil* is the most common marking tool. A pencil mark is easy to see and can be quickly removed. Use a pencil with a No. 2 lead or a hard lead.

2. A short-blade *knife* (like the sloyd knife) is used for very accurate marking and for cutting and whittling. It should be used only when cutting to (on) the line. Then the saw will remove the mark. Fig. 6-10.

6-10. Sloyd knife.

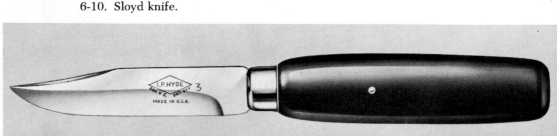

6-11. Scratch awl.

(Stanley Tools)

3. A *scratch awl* is used for marking the center for holes to be drilled or bored. It can also serve as a punch to make a small dent for starting nails, screws, brads, and cup hooks. Fig. 6-11. It is handy for scribing (drawing) lines on wood.

READING A RULE. Before using measuring tools, you must be sure that you can use the rule correctly. It isn't hard to measure in feet and exact inches. If the measurement is in feet, you place a single mark (') after the number. If the measurement is in inches only, you place a double mark (″) after the number. You already know that there are 12 inches in a foot and 3 feet (or 36 inches) in a yard.

6-12. Study this chart. It will help you to read a rule to 1/16 inch.

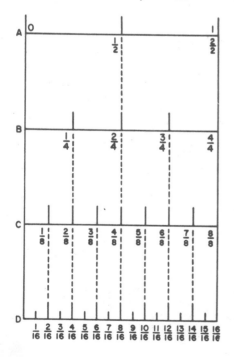

Measuring in parts (fractions) of an inch takes a little more care.

• Look at the enlarged inch shown in Fig. 6-12. Notice that the distance between 0 and 1 is 1 inch.

• Look at Line A. You see that the inch is divided in half. Each half is ½ inch (½″). This half-inch division line is the longest line between the inch marks.

• Look at Line B. Here the inch is divided into four equal parts (each part is ¼″). The first line is ¼ inch, the second is 2/4, or ½, inch, the third line is ¾ inch.

• Look at Line C. The inch is divided into eight equal parts. Each small division is ⅛ inch (⅛″). Two of these divisions make 2/8, or ¼, inch, as shown on Line B. Four of these divisions make 4/8 inch, or 2/4 inch, or ½ inch (½″). (Many rules used in woodworking are divided into only eight parts, making the smallest division ⅛ inch.)

• Look at Line D. Here the inch is divided into sixteen parts. This is usually the smallest division on rules in woodworking. Notice again that 4/16 inch is equal to 2/8 inch, or ¼ inch. One line past ¼ inch would be 5/16 inch. On your rule or square, the half-inch mark is the longest line between the inch marks. The ¼-inch (¼″) is the next longest, the ⅛-inch (⅛″) next, and the 1/16-inch (1/16″) mark is the shortest.

• To read a part, or fraction, of an inch, count the number of small divisions beyond the inch mark. Then see how many divisions there are in the inch on the rule you are using. If there

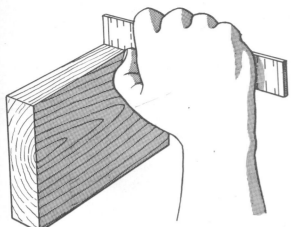

6-13. Checking the thickness of stock. Notice that one end of the rule is held over one edge of the board. The thumb slides along until you can read the thickness.

are only eight, for example, and you count five divisions, the measurement is ⅝ inch. If there are 16 divisions in the inch and you count five divisions, then the measurement is 5/16 inch. Make a line 2¼ inches long. If your rule is divided in eighths, then the line measures 2 inches plus two small divisions (2/8″). If your rule is divided into sixteenths, then this extra section

6-14. Checking the width of stock. One finger acts as a guide to hold the end of the rule even with the edge of stock. Slide the other finger along until you can read the correct width.

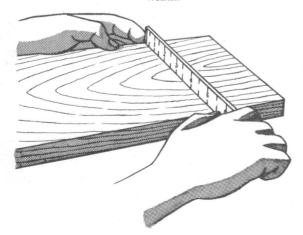

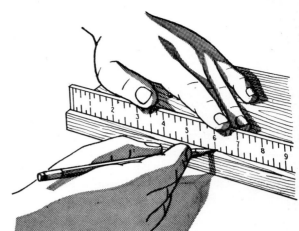

6-15. Marking to length. Note that the rule is held on edge for more accurate measurement.

is 4/16 inch, which is the same as 2/8 inch, or ¼ inch.

MEASURING

1. To check thickness, hold the rule as shown in Fig. 6-13. You can read the thickness by looking at the graduation mark directly over the corner.

2. To check width, hold the rule as shown in Fig. 6-14. Be sure the rule is at right angles to the edge.

MARKING TO LENGTH

1. Look at the end of the board. Make sure it is square and doesn't have

6-16a. Using a try square.

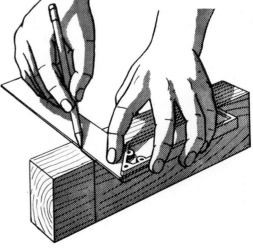

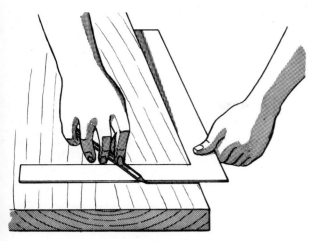

6-16b. Drawing a line across the board using a steel, or carpenter's square.

a *split*, *check* (slight separation) or other flaw. If it is not square, trim the end. (Find out from the drawing how long the board must be and then add about ½ inch for trimming and squaring up. Use the try square to test for squareness. See page 27.)

2. Hold the rule on edge and parallel to the edge of the board. Place the end of the rule exactly even with the end of the board. The rule must not be at an angle. It is held on edge so the graduation marks are right next to the surface of the wood. Fig. 6-15.

6-17. **Marking** for width. Several marks should be made at various points along the board.

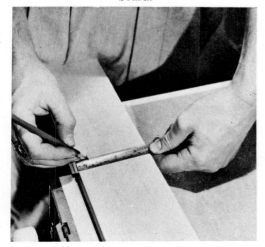

3. Use a zigzag rule or a tape rule for long boards.

4. Mark the wood at the correct length with a sharp pencil or knife. Make a small point right at the mark on the rule.

5. Place a try square so the handle is against the edge of the board. Slide the blade along until the pencil mark is just visible (just barely shows).

6. Rule a line along the board.

7. If it is a wide board, use a steel or carpenter's square instead. Fig. 6-16 a-b. Tilt the blade slightly and then hold it firmly against the edge.

MARKING FOR WIDTH

1. Find out from the drawing how wide the board must be. Allow about ⅛ to ¼ inch extra for squaring up.

2. Hold a rule at right angles to the edge and mark this width at several points. Fig. 6-17. Another method of doing this is described in Unit 7, gage-marking a line.

3. Hold a try square or carpenter's square along these points and draw the line. Fig. 6-18.

QUESTIONS

1. Name three common kinds of rules.
2. What are the three common lengths of bench rules?
3. What kind of rule is good for measuring curved surfaces?

6-18. Drawing a line with a try square before cutting to width.

4. Name four kinds of squares found in the wood shop.

5. Describe some of the things that can be done with a try square.

6. What kind of square would be useful in working on a house?

7. Which kind of square has a blade that can be removed from the handle or head?

8. Which marking tool is most often used in beginning woodworking?

9. Why is the knife best for more accurate layouts?

10. How many sixteenths are there in 1½ inch?

11. What is the smallest division found on most woodworking rules?

12. Must the end of the board be square before you can mark to length?

13. What would happen if the rule were not parallel to the edge of the board when you measured for length?

14. When marking a wide board for length, what kind of square should be used to mark a line across it?

15. About how much material must be allowed for squaring up stock?

16. Why are measuring and marking so important in starting to construct something?

Unit 7. GAGE-MARKING A LINE

Gage-marking, or scribing, means drawing a line that is parallel to a surface or edge. For example, before cutting stock to width you must scribe, or mark, a line parallel to the first edge. (Edges may be marked 1, 2, 3, etc., in the order you are to work them.) Marking usually must be done before cutting and planing. In woodwork, marking is often referred to simply as "gaging." However, gaging actually means "to find the exact measurement of," so the term gage-marking is used here.

TOOLS AND MATERIALS

• The *marking gage* is used for mark-

ing a line an equal distance along the edge or face, especially when the distance is 6 inches or less. See Fig. 7-1.

• A *pencil compass* is good for marking narrow widths.

• The *combination square* is used often for marking.

• A *rule and pencil* are also needed.

MARKING WITH A MARKING GAGE

1. Check the marking gage to make sure the *spur*, or *pin*, is a sharp wedge shape. If dull, this must be sharpened. Some types have a wheel at the end of the beam.

2. Adjust to the correct length. No-

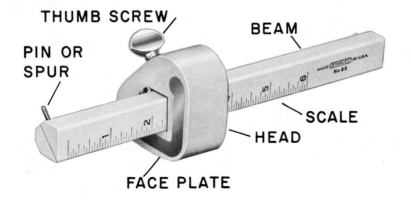

7-1. Parts of a marking gage. (Stanley Tools)

THUMB SCREW

PIN OR SPUR

BEAM

SCALE

HEAD

FACE PLATE

7-2. Setting a marking gage using a rule.

7-4. Using a combination square and pencil for marking. This is one of the simplest ways for marking to width.

tice the rule on the side of the beam. This can be used to set the distance. It will not be accurate (exactly correct), however, after you have sharpened the pin, or spur. To adjust again:

- Adjust to the distance as shown on the beam and tighten the thumb screw lightly.
- Hold the gage in your left hand with the spur up.
- Hold a rule on edge in your right hand. Place the end of the rule against the head of the gage. Fig. 7-2.
- Check the distance. A slight movement of the head in either direction will adjust it to the correct amount. Tighten the thumb screw.

3. Try the gage on a piece of scrap stock. Get the "feel" of the tool. It is better to push the tool than to pull it.

4. Tilt the gage at a slight angle. Hold the head gently, but firmly, against the surface or edge. Fig. 7-3. Push the tool away from you. *Make a shallow groove.* If you push too hard,

the point may jump out of place and scratch the surface.

5. Never mark across grain or gage for a bevel or chamfer (slanted cut) with a marking gage. (See Unit 19.)

Marking With a Pencil Compass

1. Sharpen a pencil. Put it in the compass, with the pencil section a little shorter than the metal point. (See Fig. 8-2, Unit 8.)

2. Set the width with a rule.

3. Hold the metal point against the surface of the wood as you gage the line. Keep the compass at *right angles* to the work at all times.

Marking With a Combination Square

1. Adjust the blade to the correct length measured from the right-angle side of the head.

2. Hold the head against the work and a pencil against the end of the blade. Fig. 7-4.

3. Slide both along the board to mark the line.

4. You can use a rule and pencil for gage-marking. This is a little more difficult because you must keep the rule square with the edge as you slide it along.

Gage-Marking With a Pencil Only

1. To mark a narrow distance, hold the pencil between your fingers with

7-3. Using a marking gage. .Note that the head of the gage is tipped slightly as it is pushed along.

the point extending the measured distance.

2. Rest your middle finger against the surface or edge as you push or pull the pencil along to mark the line. Fig. 7-5. Practice is needed to do this expertly.

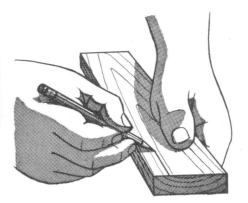

7-5. Gage-marking with a pencil. This method is good only for narrow widths such as in marking a chamfer or bevel (slanted cut). See Unit 19.

QUESTIONS

1. Define "gaging" and "marking."
2. Name the parts of a marking gage.
3. Tell how to set a marking gage to 1¾ inch.
4. Can a pencil compass be used for gage-marking? Describe how.
5. Why is a combination square a good marking tool?

Unit 8. MAKING A LAYOUT

A *layout* is a guide, or pattern, that can be drawn or traced directly on the wood for each part. The layout shows shape and size, location of holes and other openings, and all the things to be worked. For irregular shapes and designs, a *pattern,* or *template,* is often used. See Unit 9.

On some parts, the layout may be made as you work the wood, after you have more experience.

LAYOUT TOOLS

• All the tools used for *measuring* and *marking* are used in making a layout: rules, marking gage, squares, pencil, knife.
• A *dividers* is a tool with two metal legs. Fig. 8-1. It is used to lay out circles and arcs and for stepping off equal distances. To *set a dividers,* place one leg over an inch mark of the rule and open the other leg to the measurement you want. To *use a dividers,* place one leg over the punch mark, tilt the di-

viders slightly, and turn it clockwise (the direction clock hands move).
• A *pencil compass* can be used in place of a dividers in the wood shop. Fig. 8-2. It has one metal leg and one pencil leg.
• *Trammel points* are used in place of

8-1. Dividers. (Stanley Tools)

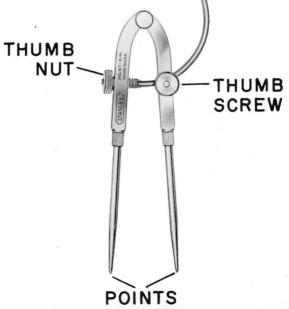

THUMB NUT

THUMB SCREW

POINTS

34

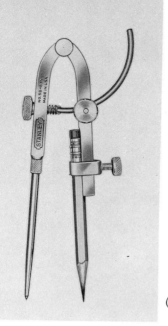

8-2. Pencil compass.

(Stanley Tools)

8-4. Accuracy is a measurement must. Place one point of the dividers over the inch mark and open until the other end reaches the point equal to the radius.

a dividers for laying out large circles and arcs. Fig. 8-3.

DRAWING A CIRCLE

1. Locate the center of the circle.
2. Adjust the dividers or compass to equal the radius (half the distance across, or diameter of, the circle) Fig. 8-4. The circumference of a circle is the distance completely around it. It is equal to the diameter times 3.1416, or 22/7.

3. Place one leg at the center mark. Tilt the dividers slightly, and swing it clockwise to draw the line or sharp groove. Fig. 8-5.
4. To keep from scratching the wood surface at the center, place a small rubber eraser over the sharp point of the dividers or compass. A piece of masking tape can be placed at the center to protect the wood.

8-5. Using a dividers to draw an arc.

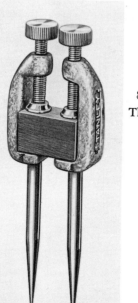

8-3. Trammel points. The points are fastened to a long bar of metal or wood. (Stanley Tools)

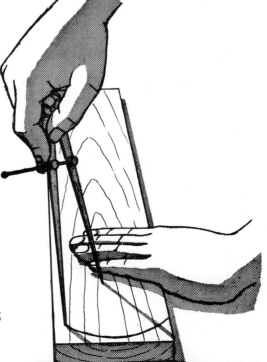

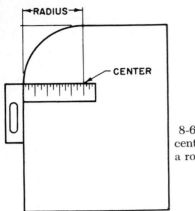

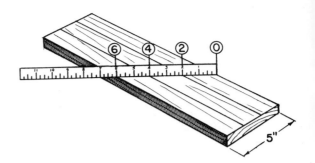

8-6. Finding the center or drawing a rounded corner.

8-8. Dividing a board into three equal parts.

DRAWING A ROUNDED CORNER. Many things are made with rounded corners to improve their appearance.

1. Find the radius of the corner.

2. Mark this distance from the corner on one side and end. Fig. 8-6.

3. Hold a try square against the side and end and draw two lines to mark the center.

4. Set the dividers to the correct radius.

5. Swing the dividers from the left to the right, or from the side to the end, clockwise, to mark the rounded corner.

LAYOUT OF DUPLICATE PARTS (**parts exactly alike**). Many articles have two or more parts that are exactly alike. Lay out these parts together, to save time.

1. Place the pieces on edge and side by side on a bench top.

2. Make sure the working ends are

8-7. Laying out duplicate parts. Mark all pieces at the same time.

even by holding a try square over the end. Hold the pieces together firmly in a vise or with a clamp. Fig. 8-7.

3. Measure the correct length along one edge.

4. Mark a line across all the pieces at the same time.

DIVIDING A BOARD INTO EQUAL PARTS. If a board is an odd width and you want to divide it into any number of equal parts, follow this simple procedure:

• Hold a rule *at an angle* across the face of the board until the inch marks divide the space evenly.

• If the board you need to divide is 5 inches wide and you want to divide it into three equal parts, hold the rule at an angle with the 6-inch mark on one edge. Then make a mark at the 2-, 4-, and 6-inch marks. Fig. 8-8.

8-9. Laying out a hexagon. This shape might be used for the base of a wastepaper basket.

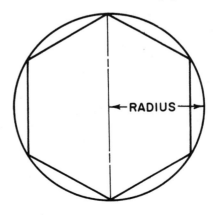

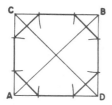

8-10. Laying out an octagon.

DRAWING A HEXAGON. A *hexagon* is a six-sided figure with equal sides and angles. This figure might be used for the bottom of a wastepaper basket, a hot dish holder, or similar article.

1. Determine the maximum (greatest) distance across the corner. Then use half this distance as the radius, or use a radius equal to one side of the hexagon.

2. Draw a circle with this radius. Fig. 8-9.

3. Start at any spot around the circle and draw an arc.

4. Continue to draw arcs, dividing the circle into six equal parts.

5. Connect these points.

DRAWING AN OCTAGON. An *octagon* has eight equal sides and angles. It might be used as the shape of a wall decoration, a stool or table top.

1. Draw a square equal to the side of the octagon.

2. Draw diagonal lines (across the corners), AB and CD, Fig. 8-10.

3. Adjust the dividers to half the length of one of the diagonal lines.

4. Using points A, B, C, and D as centers, strike arcs intersecting (cutting across) the sides.

5. Connect the points where the arcs intersect (cross each other).

8-11. Drawing an ellipse (oval) using the shop method.

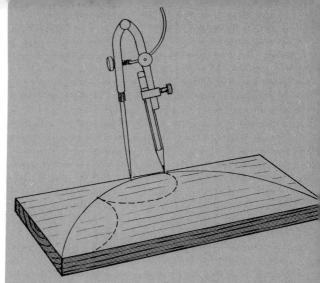

8-12. Stepping off equal distances on an arc with a dividers.

DRAWING AN ELLIPSE BY THE SHOP METHOD. An *ellipse* is an oval having both sides alike. It might be used as the shape of a table top, a plaque (wall decoration), or the back of a wall lamp.

1. Lay out the two diameters at right angles to each other.

2. Set the dividers equal to half the longest diameter.

3. Using D as center, strike (draw) an arc intersecting AB at X and Y, Fig. 8-11.

4. Place brads (small nail) at X, Y, and D. Tie a string around these three brads.

5. Take the brad at D away, and put a pencil in its place.

6. Hold the pencil tight against the string. Carefully draw the ellipse.

STEPPING OFF EQUAL DISTANCES. To step off equal distances or to divide a space into equal parts, the dividers or compass can be used. This is especially good for dividing a curved line.

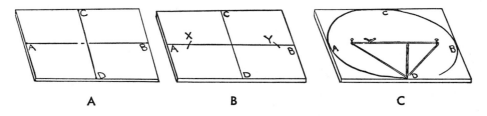

A   B   C

1. Adjust the dividers to the correct amount (usually a small, even part of the total distance).

2. Place one leg on the starting point and then turn the dividers from side to side as shown in Fig. 8-12.

Unit 9. ENLARGING A DESIGN AND USING A TEMPLATE

Often you will find the plan for a project you like in a book or magazine. The only problem is that it's less than full size. Your first job is to enlarge this pattern so that you can trace or transfer it to the wood. This is something you'll be doing often in woodworking. The steps are simple, but you need to follow them carefully to make the full-size pattern exactly like the small one.

Suppose you saw the design in Fig. 9-1 in a book. In most books and magazines the drawing is laid out in squares. A note tells you what size the full-size squares must be. Sometimes, however,

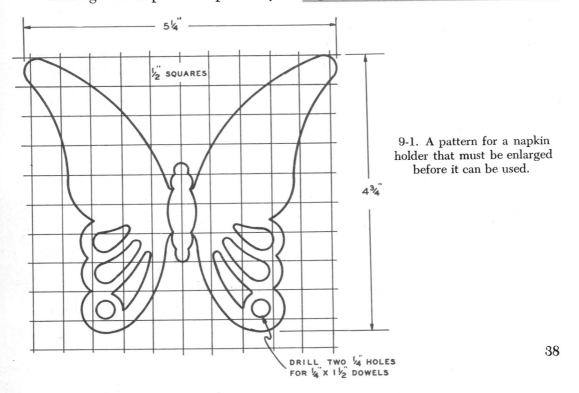

9-1. A pattern for a napkin holder that must be enlarged before it can be used.

5¼"

½" SQUARES

4¾"

DRILL TWO ¼" HOLES FOR ¼" X 1½" DOWELS

38

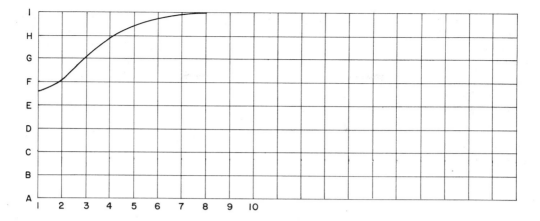

you find a drawing or photograph that has no squares. If the design is about ¼ the size you would like to have it, first cover it with ¼-inch squares. If the design is in a book, draw the squares on transparent paper (you can see through it) and clip the paper over the page. Now proceed as follows:

1. On a large piece of paper, draw squares the full size. (You can also use cross-sectioned paper.) For example, if the drawing says, "one-inch squares", make your squares this size. Start in the lower lefthand corner of both the original drawing and the full-size sheet. Letter up the left side A, B, C, etc.

9-3. (a) Using a template to trace a pattern.

9-2. Enlarging a fish design for making a cutting board.

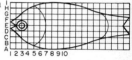

Number across the bottom 1, 2, 3, etc. Fig. 9-2.

2. Locate points on the drawing. Transfer them to the full-size pattern. Continue to locate enough points to make the outline take shape.

3. After enough points are located, use a French curve (also called an ir-regular curve) to trace the outline. Fig. 9-3a. You can also bend a piece of soft wire (such as solder) to follow the various points. Trace the line.

4. If the design is the same on both sides (a symmetrical plan), you need to trace only half the pattern. Then fold the paper down the center. Cut out the full pattern or trace the full pattern by

(b) This piece could be used as a template to make many others of the same shape.

placing carbon paper between the folds, carbon side facing toward the blank half.

5. A design can be made smaller by reversing the above procedure.

6. You can use this full-size plan in one of several ways:

a. Cut out the plan with scissors, fasten corners with transparent tape, and trace around it on the wood. Then remove.

b. Cut out the pattern with scissors and paste or glue it on the wood. It stays on while the wood is trimmed to size.

c. Place carbon paper between the pattern and the wood and trace the design. Then remove.

7. When many parts of the same design are to be made, a *template* (a pattern that can be used many times) is made of thin wood or metal. Hold the template firmly on the wood and trace around it. Fig. 9-3b.

QUESTIONS

1. What must be done if the design is not full size?
2. If the plan is one third as large as you want it and it is covered with ¼-inch squares, how large must the full-size squares be?
3. Tell how to use a pattern in making a layout on wood.
4. What is a template?
5. How is a template used?

HOW MACHINES HELP YOU IN WOODWORKING

You probably know that complicated devices such as the drill press and jig saw are *machines*. However, you might be surprised to learn that the hand tools you will use in the shop are also machines. Chisels, hammers—even things like a nail or screw—are machines, operated with hand power. Each of these simple items is just as truly a machine as the more complicated ones. As a matter of fact, the machines such as the jig saw are made up of several very simple machines fitted together in different ways.

What is a machine? A *machine* is a device used to make *work* easier. It is really a device used to apply force to good advantage. As you use hand tools, materials and machines in woodwork you will be doing work. What do we mean by *work*? *Work* is done when a force moves through a distance to make something move or stop moving. You are "working" when you strike a ball with a bat or when you ride a bicycle. You are also doing work when you pound a nail or saw a board. *Force* is the push or pull that can do work. A simple machine helps you work by multiplying the force you use. Such a gain of force is obtained by "trading" distance. For example, try turning a screw into wood with your fingers. Can you do it? Now use a screw driver. How can such a simple machine (wheel and axle) help you do work? Easy. You apply force to the handle. The outside of the handle moves a *greater distance* with less force so that the tip of the blade moves a *shorter distance* with more force.

By exerting a force on a machine in one place, the machine can exert a force at another place and, in some cases, in another direction. Look at the bicycle. You apply an up-and-down force with your knee while your foot goes around in a circle. The force applied to the pedals turns the large gear wheel. The big and little gear wheels are connected with a chain. The small gear wheel turns the rear

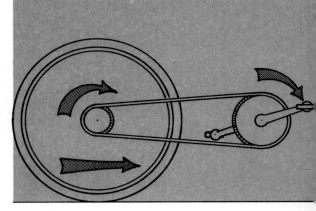

wheel to move the bicycle *forward*. The bicycle changes the direction of the force. The force also is decreased to increase speed. You can never get more out of a machine than you put in. In fact, some force is lost through the *friction* of the machine. *Friction* is the rubbing together of machine parts. No machine can increase both force and distance at the same time. The screw-driver tip has greater force but moves through less distance than the handle. The rear wheel of the bicycle moves through greater distance but has less force than that applied to the pedals.

There are six simple *machines*. All complicated machines are made up of a combination of these:

1. The *inclined plane* makes work easier, since a smaller effort (the force exerted) can lift a heavy weight. However, the effort must move farther (along the incline) than when a weight is lifted directly.

2. A *wedge* has one or two sloping sides. All knives, chisels, saws, and axles have wedges.

3. A *screw* is actually a spiral-shaped inclined plane. A wood screw clamp or vise is a good example of the screw.

4. A *lever* is a long, rigid bar supported at one point, called the fulcrum. The hammer and axe are levers.

Simple Machine	A Few Places Where You Will Find It Used
1. Inclined Plane 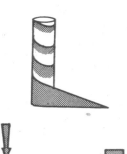	Parts of a plane, chisel, or gouge
2. Wedge	Cutting edge of chisel, knife, or gouge Teeth of saw or file Nail Plane iron blade
3. Screw	Wood screw Parts of a vise, hand clamp, C clamp or bar clamp
4. Lever	Hammer Hinge Pliers Paintbrush

5. Wheel and Axle

Brace   Hand drill
Screw driver

6. Pulley

Parts of a band saw, belt sander, or jig saw

5. The *wheel-and-axle has a* wheel connected firmly to an axle. When one turns, the other turns too. A screw driver, a door handle, and a brace are examples of the wheel and axle.

6. A *pulley* is a wheel that turns around an axle.

Remember these six machines. As you look through this book you'll see how woodworking tools are based on them.

Unit 10. SAWING TO A LINE WITH HAND SAWS

A *saw* is a wood-cutting tool that has a thin steel blade with small sharp teeth along the edge. Hand saws are used to cut wood to different sizes and shapes. They are also used for making the joints that hold parts together. Your skill in using hand saws is important because it shows in the final appearance of the project.

TOOLS

• The *crosscut saw* is used to saw across grain. The parts are shown in Fig. 10-1. The teeth are knife-shaped and bent alternately to the right and left. Fig. 10-2. This is called *set*. It makes the saw cut wider than the blade. The saw cut is called the *kerf*. Since the kerf is wider than the blade, the blade will not bind (stick) as the sawing is done. The saw teeth may be coarse (with only four or five teeth per inch) or fine (with as many as ten

Sawing a board. Remember the six basic machines. The teeth of a hand saw are *wedges*. The saw itself is a *lever* in your hand. Notice that the wedges are shaped to cut on the down, or forward, stroke. Here again the force applied to the handle is divided into smaller forces that make each tooth (wedge) do the cutting. See pages 41 and 42.

or twelve per inch). A saw for general-purpose cutting should have about eight or nine *points* per inch (there is

POINTS TO THE INCH

"Points to the inch" is the term used to designate the size of the teeth in a saw. The smaller the number of teeth to the inch the rougher the cut; the greater the number of teeth, the smoother the cut.

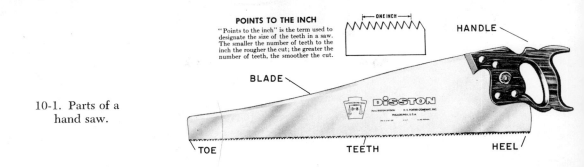

HANDLE

BLADE

TOE   TEETH   HEEL

10-1. Parts of a hand saw.

10-2. A crosscut saw is used to cut across grain. Notice the knife-shaped teeth.

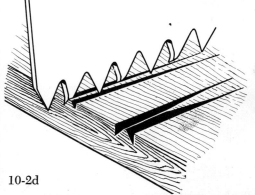

10-2d

45°

10-2b. Angle for cross cutting.

10-3. (a) A rip saw is used to cut with the grain. It has chisel-shaped teeth.

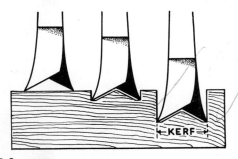

←KERF→

10-2c

one more point than teeth per inch) and should be about 24 inches long.

• The *rip saw* is used for sawing with the grain. The teeth are chisel-shaped and are set alternately to the right and left. Fig. 10-3. A 24-inch, 5½-point saw is a good one for most work.

• A *wood vise* is a clamping device for holding the wood to the bench for saw-

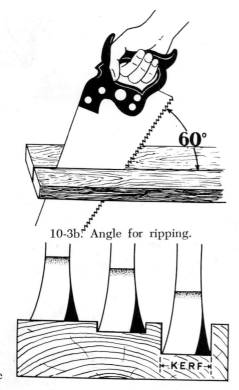

10-3b. Angle for ripping.

10-3c

10-3d. The rip saw cuts with many small chisels. First a tooth on one side cuts a small piece free and then the tooth on the other side cuts a similar piece.

short turn of the handle tightens the jaws. There is a *dog* (section) in the movable jaw that can be raised. A *bench stop* can be inserted in holes along the top of the bench. The work is held between a dog and bench stop when cutting or planing.

• A *sawhorse* is a support on which the carpenter or woodworker places the lumber for cutting. Fig. 10-5. One or two are needed.

Cutting With a Hand Saw

1. Lay out the cutoff line across the board with a pencil. When cutting used

ing and other work. Fig. 10-4. The vise is lined with wood to protect the work. The movable jaw moves on a continuous thread so the jaws can be opened or closed by turning the handle. There is another type of wood vise that has quick action. The movable jaw is pushed closed on the work and then a

10-4. (a) A wood vise is used to hold the stock when cutting short pieces. (b) The vise is mounted on a sturdy bench.

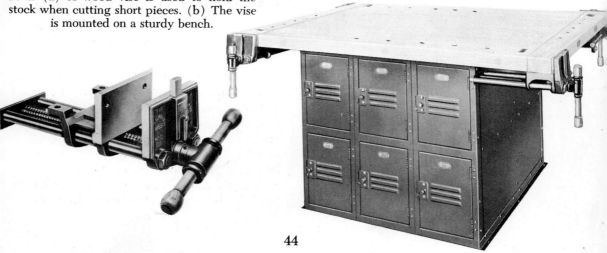

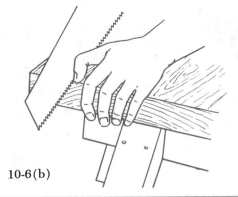

10-6(b)

10-5. When cutting large pieces, place the lumber over one or two sawhorses.

or old lumber, be sure all nails and screws have been removed.

2. Place the board in a vise or over one or more sawhorses. The cutoff line must be outside the supports, never between.

3. Hold the handle of the crosscut saw in your right hand, with the index finger extended to support it. If *left-handed*, the same is true.

4. Place your free hand on the board, using your thumb as a guide

10-6. (a) Using your thumb as a guide to get the saw started.

for the saw blade. Fig. 10-6. Keep in mind that the kerf should be in the waste stock.

5. Start the cut by pulling back on the saw once or twice. Be careful that the saw doesn't jump and cut your thumb.

6. After the kerf is started, hold the saw at an angle of 45 or 60 degrees to the surface. Move your hand away from the blade. Fig. 10-7. Take long, uniform (even) strokes.

7. Sight along the saw or check with the try square to make sure you are making a square cut. Fig. 10-8, page 46.

8. As you cut, watch the layout line, not the saw. Blow the sawdust away.

9. If the saw is moving into or away from the line, twist the handle slightly to bring it back.

10. As the final strokes are made, hold the end to be cut off. If you don't do this, the corner will split out as the piece drops. Fig. 10-9. Never twist off thin strips of wood with the saw blade.

10-7. Move your hand away and hold the saw at an angle of 45 or 60 degrees.

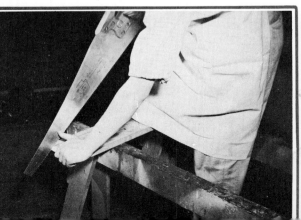

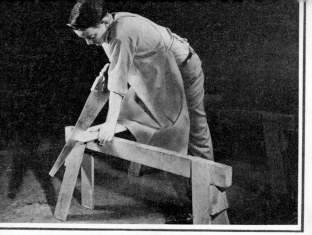

10-8. Sight along the saw to keep it cutting straight.

10-10. Ripping with the stock held in a vise.

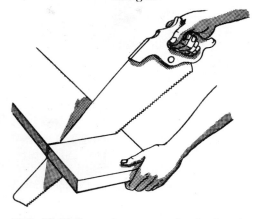

10-9. Hold the end as you make the last few saw cuts.

CUTTING IN A VISE

1. Fasten shorter boards in the vise with the layout line vertical (up and down) and slightly to the left of the vise jaw. If the board is quite long, clamp it near the top in the jaws at first and then move it up as you cut. Fig. 10-10.

2. Place longer boards over one or two sawhorses.

3. Start by taking short strokes *backward only*.

4. After the kerf is started, hold the saw at an angle of 45 or 60 degrees. Sometimes on a long cut, the kerf tends to close behind the saw, causing the blade to bind. If this happens place a small wedge in the kerf to keep it open.

QUESTIONS

1. What kind of saw must be used to cut across grain? With the grain?

2. What do you call the groove cut by a saw?

3. Why are the teeth of the saw wider than the saw itself?

4. Describe the kind of saw you might buy for general use in a home workshop.

5. Is the saw cut started by pushing or pulling?

6. How should you guide the saw when starting a cut?

7. At about what angle should the saw be held for cutting across grain?

8. Which should you watch when the cutting is done, the layout line or the saw?

9. Why should the end of the board be held while the last few strokes are made?

10. At about what angle do you hold a saw when cutting with the grain?

11. When cutting a long board with a rip saw, what can you do if the saw starts to bind?

Unit 11. ASSEMBLING AND ADJUSTING A PLANE

11-1. Select the right plane for the job.

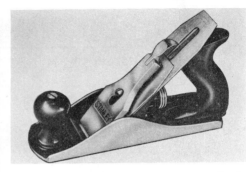

11-3. The smooth plane is best for small jobs. (Stanley Tools)

A *plane* is a special tool with a blade for smoothing and removing wood as shavings. The modern plane developed from the chisel. The plane is nothing more than a chisel held in a block of metal so it can be controlled to take an even cut. This is one tool you'll use a lot. Fig. 11-1. It takes patience to learn to adjust and use it correctly. Even more skill is needed to sharpen the cutting tool correctly, yet a plane works well only if the blade is sharp and adjusted correctly. Even then it will smooth a surface only if it is used in the right way.

KINDS OF BENCH PLANES

• The *jack plane* ("Jack of all trades")

is the most common plane. It is either 14 or 15 inches long, with a 2-inch blade. It is ideal for rough surfaces that require a heavier chip. It is also good for obtaining a smooth and flat surface. Fig. 11-2.
• A slightly narrower and shorter plane is the *junior jack plane*. It is 11½ inches long with a 1¾-inch blade.
• A *smooth plane* is 7 to 9 inches long and is used for smaller work. It is a good plane for general use around the home. Fig. 11-3.
• A *fore plane* is longer (18 inches) and is used to plane long surfaces and edges. Fig. 11-4.
• The largest plane is called a *jointer plane*. It is 22 or 24 inches long and is used by carpenters for planing long boards such as the edges of doors.

11-2. The jack plane is the most useful, all-around tool for both rough surfaces and smooth flat surfaces. (Stanley Tools)

11-4. The fore plane is needed for planing long and straight edges. (Stanley Tools)

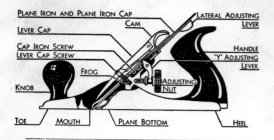

11-5. (a) Parts of a plane. (b) Uses of the working parts. (Stanley Tools)

cap screw. Now carefully lift the *double plane iron* out of the plane. Notice that this is made in two parts, the top one called the *plane-iron cap.* It breaks the chips and forces the chips or shavings up and out. The lower edge is called the *chip break.* The actual cutting blade is called a *single plane iron.* It must be kept sharp as described in Unit 17. The part that supports the double plane iron is called the *frog.* There is an *adjusting nut* for changing

LATERAL ADJUSTING LEVER SETS CUTTING EDGE PARALLEL TO BOTTOM

PLANE IRON BLADE DOES THE CUTTING

PLANE IRON CAP STIFFENS PLANE IRON BLADE, AND CURLS SHAVINGS

LEVER CAP

ADJUSTING NUT FOR DEPTH OF CUT

FROG SUPPORTS PLANE IRON BLADE AND PLANE IRON CAP

LEVER CAP ADJUSTING SCREW SETS LEVER FOR CORRECT TENSION

GETTING ACQUAINTED WITH THE JACK PLANE. The plane is the most complicated hand tool you will use. You should learn the major parts and how to adjust it. Let's look at the hand plane in Fig. 11-5. The main part is called the *body,* or *bed,* and the wide flat is called the *bottom.* The back of the bottom is the *heel* and the front is the *toe.* The opening across the bottom is called the *mouth,* or *throat.* The *knob* (in front) is held in one hand and the *handle* (in back) in the other hand. Lift up on the *cam lever* to release the *lever cap.* Then slide the lever cap up and it will come off over the *lever*

the depth of the cut. A *lateral adjusting lever* can be moved to the right or left so that the cutting edge will be straight (parallel to the bottom).

HOW TO PUT THE DOUBLE PLANE IRON TOGETHER

1. Hold the single plane iron in your left hand with the bevel side of the blade down.

2. Hold the plane-iron cap crosswise and drop the cap screw through the hole. (Fig. 11-6 (1).

3. Slide the plane-iron cap away from the cutting edge (Fig. 11-6 (2) and rotate it ¼ turn so that it is

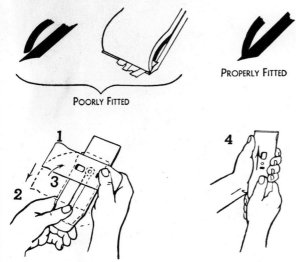

POORLY FITTED

PROPERLY FITTED

11-6. The steps in assembling a double plane iron. Note that the plane-iron cap must fit the plane iron tightly. If it doesn't, chips get between the two parts and cause poor planing action. (Stanley Tools)

straight with the plane iron. Fig. 11-6 (3).

4. Carefully slide the cap forward, guiding it with your left thumb and forefinger. Fig. 11-6 (4). Be careful not to slip the cap over the cutting edge, as this might nick it. The cap should be about 1/16 inch from the cutting edge for most work. For very fine planing, about 1/32 inch is better.

5. Hold the two parts together, and then tighten the cap screw with a screw driver or the lever cap. Be sure the two parts are good and tight. If chips get between the plane iron and the cap, you'll have trouble planing. Fig. 11-6.

PUTTING THE DOUBLE PLANE IRON IN THE PLANE

1. Place the plane upright on the

11-7. Steps in installing a double plane iron in the plane: (a) The double plane iron is assembled and placed over the frog. (b) The plane iron is in place and the plane-iron cap is inserted. (c) The plane-iron cap holds the double plane iron firmly in place.

bench with a small scrap of wood under the toe to raise one end of the bottom. This is done to protect the cutting edge. *Make sure the cutting edge never comes in contact with metal.*

2. Hold the double plane iron with the cap up. Carefully guide the cutter into the plane and over the lever cap screw. Be careful not to hit the cutting edge on the side of the plane. Fig. 11-7 (a).

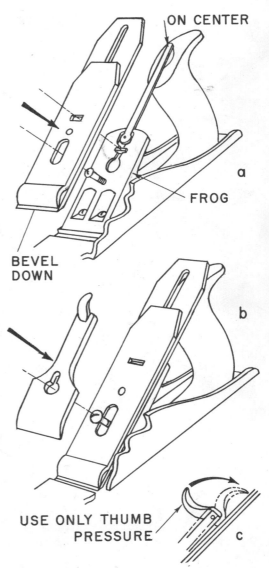

ON CENTER

FROG

a

BEVEL DOWN

b

USE ONLY THUMB PRESSURE

c

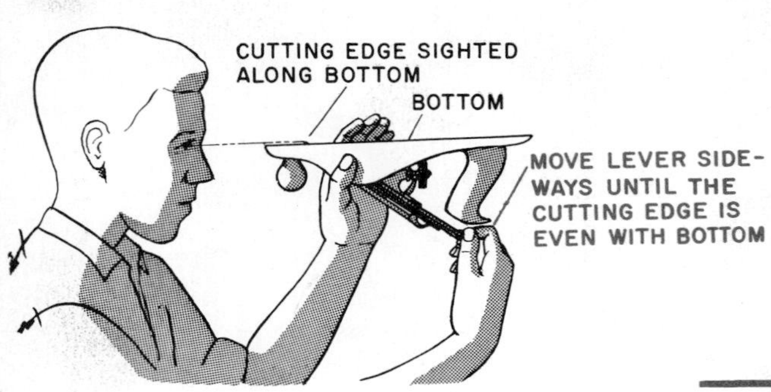

CUTTING EDGE SIGHTED
ALONG BOTTOM
BOTTOM

MOVE LEVER SIDE-
WAYS UNTIL THE
CUTTING EDGE IS
EVEN WITH BOTTOM

11-8. Adjusting the plane. Sighting along the bottom of the plane to make sure the cutting edge is parallel to the bottom.

a

b

c

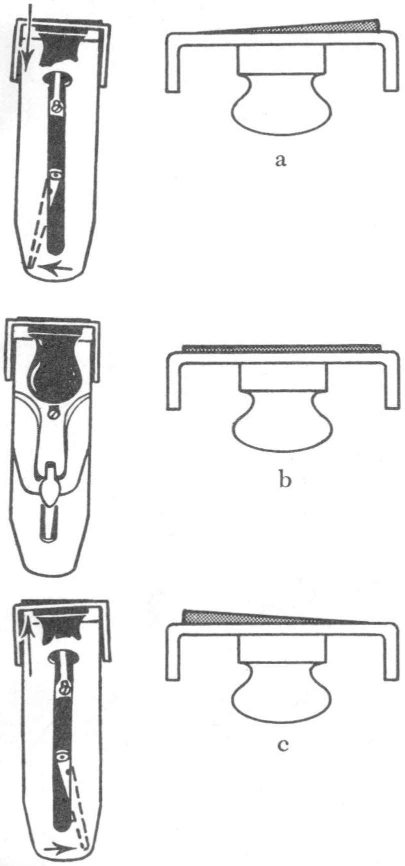

11-9. (a) Moving the lateral adjustment lever to the left raises the right side of the plane iron. (b) The plane iron is parallel to the bottom. (c) Moving the lateral adjustment lever to the right raises the left side of the plane iron.

3. Now make sure that (a) the long slot in the plane iron fits over the roller of the lateral adjusting lever, and (b) the small slot in the plane-iron cap fits over the depth of cut or Y adjusting lever. Both must be in place before you can adjust the plane. Fig. 11-7 (b).

4. Slip the lever cap in place and push the cap down. The cap should hold the double plane iron snugly. Fig. 11-7 (c). If it is too tight, it will be hard to adjust the plane. If it is too loose, the plane won't stay in adjustment. You can tighten or loosen the lever cap screw (with a screw driver or the cap) until the clamp lever will close with a little push.

ADJUSTING THE PLANE

1. Turn the plane upside down, holding the knob in your left hand.

2. Look or sight along the bottom. It's a good idea to face a window.

3. Turn the *adjusting nut* with your right hand until the cutting edge appears. It should stick out about the thickness of a hair.

4. Now move the *lateral adjusting lever* to the left or right until the cutting edge is parallel to the bottom. Fig. 11-8.

5. Turn the adjusting nut again until the blade just appears above the bottom. Fig. 11-9.

6. Try the plane on a piece of scrap stock. Continue to adjust it until you are satisfied with the thickness of the chip. The shaving should be smooth, silky, and of uniform (even) thickness. Fig. 11-10.

7. Always place the plane on the bench on its side—*never on the bot-*

11-10. Here is the kind of shavings you should get when you use a good plane that is correctly adjusted.

11-11. Always place the plane on its side when not in use.

tom. Fig. 11-11. The cutting edge will be damaged if you put the tool down in an upright position. Even worse is to place it in a pile on top of other hand tools.

QUESTIONS

1. Name three things that must be true before you can get a smooth surface with a plane.

2. Which are the largest and smallest planes found in the wood shop?

3. Which is the most common type of plane for general work?

4. Why should you learn the main parts of the plane?

5. What do you do to change the depth of cut?

6. Which adjustment changes the blade so it is straight, or parallel to the bottom?

7. When assembling a double plane iron, what must you watch for to prevent the cutting edge from becoming nicked?

8. For most work about how far should the cap be set from the cutting edge?

9. What tools can be used to tighten a cap screw?

10. Why should one end of the bottom of a plane be kept off the bench surface when intalling the double plane iron?

11. Describe the way to install the double plane iron in the plane.

Unit 12. PLANING THE FIRST SURFACE

In squaring up stock, the *first*, or *face*, surface should be planed first. Usually you will start with the widest surface that requires the least amount of planing.

12-A1. Planing wood. Remember the six basic machines, page 41. The plane is made up of several of the basic machines. Here, the plane blade (a wedge) is cutting the chip. The cap is an inclined plane to help the chip slide out of the way. Look at the plane. You'll find a *wheel and axle*, several *levers*, and some *screws*. The plane is the most complicated hand machine.

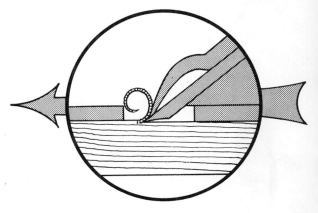

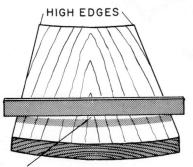

HIGH EDGES

LIGHT SHOWS UNDER STICK

12-1. Curvature in a board caused by warping.

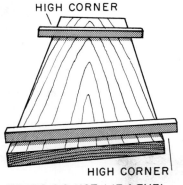

HIGH CORNER

HIGH CORNER

STICKS DO NOT LIE LEVEL

12-2. Two sticks placed across either end of the board show wind or twist.

TOOLS.—Jack plane, try square or straightedge (rule), vise, bench, and bench stop.

PLANING THE FIRST SURFACE

1. Check the stock and choose the best of the two largest surfaces. Check the board for three things:

• **Warp.** A board is warped if it is cupped so that one side is concave (dished in) and the other side is convex (rounded outward). With a pencil, mark the high spots that must be planed. Fig. 12-1.

• **Wind.** A board has wind if it twists along its length. You can check this by placing two broad sticks on the

DIRECTION OF GRAIN

12-3. Grain direction: the direction in which the planing should be done.

board and sighting along them. Another way is to place the board on a flat surface. If it has wind, it will rock on two corners. Fig. 12-2.

• **Grain direction.** If possible, decide the direction of the grain. Always plane with the grain, never against it. Planing against the grain roughens the wood. Fig. 12-3. It is difficult to see grain direction on a rough board.

2. Clamp the work so it is held securely. There are several ways to do this:

• Place a *bench stop* in a hole in the bench and place the work on the bench with the end grain against it. The work must be centered or it will slip as you begin to plane. Fig. 12-4. Clamp the work between a bench stop and the *vise dog*.

• Place the work against a board fastened to the end of the bench. Fig. 12-5.

3. Stand with your feet apart (left foot forward) and your right side near the bench. *Lefthanded persons* reverse the procedure.

12-4. The board is clamped between the vise dog and a bench stop (or pin).

BENCH STOP

VISE DOG

52

12-5. A long board is surfaced with the jointer plane. The end of the board is placed against a stop fastened to the bench.

4. Hold the knob firmly in your left hand and the handle in your right.

5. Place the toe of the plane over the end of the board. Push down on the knob as you start the stroke.

6. As the whole plane comes onto the board, apply equal pressure on both the knob and handle. As the toe of the plane leaves the board, apply more pressure to the handle. This kind of stroke will keep the surface level from one end to the other. Fig. 12-6.

7. Lift the plane on the return stroke. If you drag it back, it will roughen the surface and dull the cutting edge.

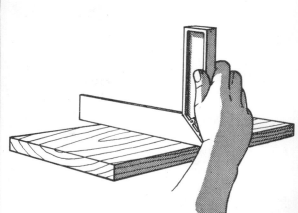

12-7. Check the surface for flatness with a try square. Check from edge to edge and diagonally across the corners.

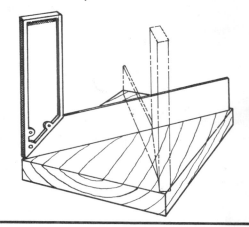

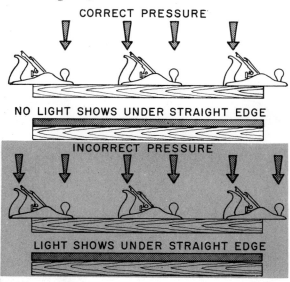

CORRECT PRESSURE

NO LIGHT SHOWS UNDER STRAIGHT EDGE

INCORRECT PRESSURE

LIGHT SHOWS UNDER STRAIGHT EDGE

8. After the first few strokes you'll be able to tell for sure if you're planing with the grain.

9. Start at one edge of the board and make a series of strokes until you reach the other side. *Always place the plane on its side when not in use.*

10. Test the surface with the try square or straightedge in several directions as shown in Fig. 12-7.

11. If there are high spots, mark these with a pencil. Then make heavy cuts diagonally across the board. Re-

12-6. The correct and incorrect method of applying pressure when planing. If the pressure is wrong, the surface will be high in the center.

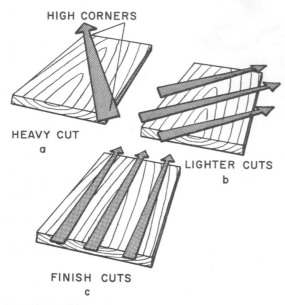

HIGH CORNERS

HEAVY CUT
a

LIGHTER CUTS
b

FINISH CUTS
c

12-8. (a) Making a heavy cut at an angle across the board to remove the high spots. (b) Reduce the depth of cut and plane in the opposite direction, taking off the other high spots. (c) Plane with the grain to smooth the surface.

duce the depth of cut and plane in the opposite direction until the high points are removed. Then plane straight along the board. Fig. 12-8.

12. If only the end towards you must be planed, start the stroke as before. Then, as you near the end of the area, slowly lift up on the handle to stop the shaving gradually.

13. If the end away from you must be planed, start the stroke with the toe of the plane against the surface and the heel held high. Gradually lower the plane as the stroke is made.

14. Mark the face surface near the first edge to be planed.

Questions

1. Which surface should you choose for the first, or face, surface?
2. Describe warp.
3. What is wind in a board?
4. Can you usually see the grain direction?
5. Describe how to stand when planing a board.
6. Why must the pressure on a plane change from the start to the end of the stroke?
7. How do you test the surface to make sure it is true?

Unit 13. PLANING THE FIRST EDGE

The *first*, or *face*, *edge* must be planed straight and smooth. It must be at right angles (square) to the face surface. Always choose the best edge to plane first. You'll be measuring from this edge for all of the other steps.

Tools. Jack plane or jointer plane, try square, vise, and hand clamp.

PLANING THE FIRST EDGE

1. Clamp the work in the vise with the edge about 2 or 3 inches above the jaw. Fig. 13-1. If the piece is long, support the other end with a hand clamp. Also, use a jointer plane on long boards. Notice how a long plane bridges (reaches across) the low spots. Fig. 13-2.

2. Hold the plane at right angles to the face surface and make a long, even stroke. Fig. 13-3. It is very important to keep the plane level or square with

13-1. Fastening the board in the vise. Select a plane and adjust it for a fine cut.

13-2. Notice that the plane with a long bed will straighten out the edge.

13-3. The smooth plane is being used to remove the rough surface. The fore plane will be used to plane the edge.

13-4. One method of holding the plane to keep it square with the face surface. The board is held against a V block.

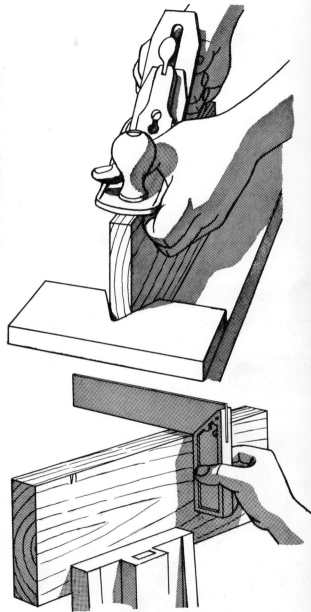

the face surface. To help guide the plane, you may hold the toe end as shown in Fig. 13-4. Curl your thumb around the back of the knob and place your fingers against the bottom. Take a light cut.

3. Continue to plane until a uniform shaving comes off the edge. To get the edge square and the surface smooth, remove as little stock as possible.

4. Remove the board from the vise. Hold the handle of a try square against the face surface to check for squareness at several places along the entire edge. Fig. 13-5.

13-5. Testing the edge for squareness. Notice also the face mark used to show which is the face surface and which is the face edge.

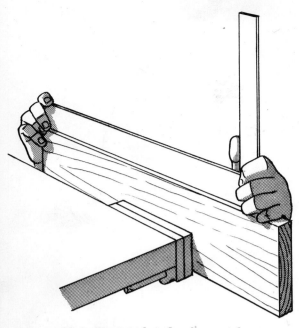

13-6. Testing the edge for straightness.

5. It is also a good idea to test for straightness. Hold a straightedge along the edge from one end to the other. Fig. 13-6.

6. Mark the *first*, or *face*, *surface* and *face edge* with a face mark as shown in Fig. 13-5. This mark will be your guide in making measurements to square up stock.

QUESTIONS

1. The first edge should be at what angle to the face surface?

2. Which edge would you choose to plane first?

3. Describe two ways of holding the front of the plane for planing an edge.

4. Describe how to check the first edge to see if it is square with the face surface.

5. Why do you mark the face surface to show that the edge has been planed?

Unit 14. PLANING END GRAIN

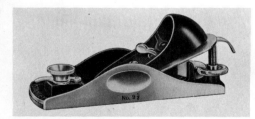

14-1. Parts of a block plane. (Stanley Tools)

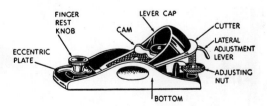

End grain is more difficult to plane because you are shearing through the wood fibers. Planing end grain is like shaving off whiskers. End grain requires planing because sawing has left it very rough. However, it doesn't have to be planed if the end of the board won't show in the finished project.

TOOLS

• A *block plane* is a small plane that has a low-angle cutter. Fig. 14-1. It is designed to cut the end grain of wood. Because of its low angle, the cutter is set bevel up. The cutter is a single plane iron with no chip breaker. The block plane is also useful for general-purpose planing. Since the tool is held in one hand, the work can be held in the other. For example, it is a good

14-2. Using a block plane to plane a chamfer.

14-4. Notice the piece of waste stock. This makes it possible to plane all the way across the end from one direction.

plane for shaping a ship-model hull or for planing a chamfer. Fig. 14-2. To adjust the cutter for thickness, sight along the plane bottom. Turn the adjusting screw to push the cutter out or to pull it in. To adjust the cutter for evenness of shaving, sight along the bottom. Move the lateral adjusting lever to the

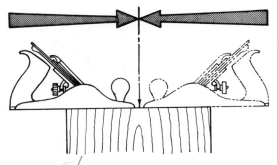

14-3. (a) The correct way to plane end grain by planing halfway across the stock. (b) This is what happens if you plane toward the outer edge.

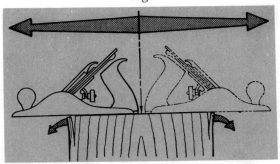

right or left as necessary.
• *Jack* or *smooth plane* and *try square*.

PLANING END GRAIN

1. Choose the end that needs the least amount of planing. Mark a sharp line across the face surface and edge as a guide.

2. Clamp the work in the vise with about 1 inch of the end grain showing. Don't plane end grain with the board sticking out too far from the vise. The work will vibrate and the cutting tool will jump.

3. The plane must be very sharp and the cap set close to the cutting edge. Adjust the depth of cut as thin as possible.

4. If you plane completely across end grain, the back edge will split off. There are three ways to avoid this:

a. Plane halfway across the end; then lift the heel. This will feather the shaving (thin it out). Then plane from the other edge. Fig. 14-3.

b. Select a piece of waste stock the same thickness as the board. Place it behind the board. Fig. 14-4.

c. Plane a short chamfer in the waste stock on the opposite edge. Then you can plane all the way in one direction.

5. Readjust the plane to a very light

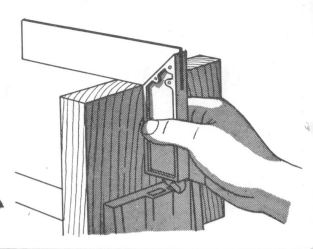

14-5. Testing the end from the face surface and face edge to make sure it is square.

cut. Hold the plane at a slight angle and take a shearing cut. Try to plane an even surface that will look good when a finish is applied.

6. Check the end with a try square from both the face surface and edge. Fig. 14-5. Put an "X" in pencil on the end so that you know it has been planed.

7. The block plane works well on end grain because the blade is held at a lower angle to the surface.

QUESTIONS

1. Why is end grain more difficult to plane?
2. Why is a block plane a good tool for planing end grain?
3. Does end grain always have to be planed? Explain.
4. Which end should be planed first?
5. Describe two ways of planing end grain.
6. Why must a light cut be made when planing end grain?

Unit 15. USING A BACK SAW

A back saw is used for fine sawing, especially when making joints or squaring up stock. The thin blade and fine teeth make a small kerf and leave a smooth surface.

TOOLS

• The *back saw* is a fine-tooth crosscut saw. It gets this name because it has a heavy metal band along the back that supports the thin blade. Fig. 15-1.

• A *bench hook* is a wood board with a cleat slightly shorter than the width

15-1. Parts of a back saw.

58

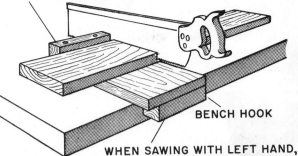

USE THIS CLEAT, AS SHOWN, WHEN
SAWING WITH RIGHT HAND

BENCH HOOK

15-2. A bench hook in use.

WHEN SAWING WITH LEFT HAND,
TURN BENCH HOOK OVER, AND
HOLD WOOD AGAINST THIS CLEAT

BOTH CLEATS ARE SHORTER THAN WIDTH OF THE
HOOK, & ARE SET TO RIGHT OR LEFT OF CENTER

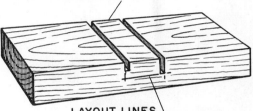

KERFS IN WASTE STOCK

LAYOUT LINES

15-3. Make the cut at the layout line but in
the waste stock.

of the board across the ends, one on either side. It is used on the bench top for such jobs as cutting and chiseling, to give support to the work, and to protect the bench. Fig. 15-2.

CUTTING WITH A BACK SAW

1. Carefully mark the location of the cut.
2. Place the bench hook over the top of the bench.
3. Hold the saw in your right hand and the work against the bench hook with the layout line to the right. If left-handed, reverse. Make sure the kerf will be in the waste stock. Fig. 15-3.
4. Use your thumb as a guide and start the cut with the handle held high.
5. As the cut is started, lower the blade a little at a time until the saw is parallel with the surface. Fig. 15-4.
6. Continue to cut until the correct depth is reached or the waste stock is cut off.
7. To help the saw make an accurate cut, clamp a smooth piece of scrap stock right next to the layout line. Fig. 32-3. Then you can hold the saw with both hands to start the cut. Don't start with the handle held high. By keeping the blade flat against the guide board,

the cut will be in the correct location and square with the surface.

QUESTIONS

1. How does the back saw get its name?
2. What is a bench hook?
3. Where should the kerf be made in the wood?
4. Why should the handle of the saw be held high when starting a cut?
5. Describe the way to make a more accurate cut with the back saw.

15-4. Cutting with a back saw.

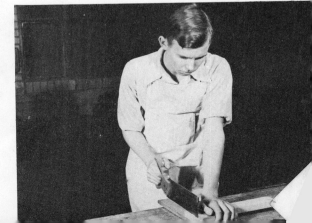

Unit 16. SQUARING UP STOCK

Rough lumber is sometimes used in building construction and repair work but never for small articles. Most of the lumber you use will be S2S, or surfaced two sides. This lumber will have to be planed very little on the surface. On plywood, you may only have to plane the four edges (all the edges are the same in plywood). At other times you might have to plane two surfaces and one edge; for example, when cutting out a design. In other cases, when the ends don't show, both surfaces and edges are planed and the ends cut to length with a saw. There will be many times, however, when you must completely square up stock. The top of a stool or small table is a good example of this. Squaring up stock is something every good woodworker must learn to do well. There are six steps.

TOOLS. Jack or smooth plane, fore plane and block plane, try square, rule, pencil, marking gage, and straightedge.

SQUARING UP STOCK

1. Plane the first, or face, surface true and smooth. Fig. 16-1.
2. Plane the first, or face, edge. Mark the face surface and edge.
3. Plane the first end.
4. Measure the correct length and mark a line across the face surface and end. Use a back saw and cut about 1/16 inch longer than the finished length. Plane the second end to correct length.
5. Plane to correct width. If the board is rather narrow, adjust the marking gage to the correct width and mark a line along the face surface and the second surface. You can also use the other methods of gaging as described in Unit 7. If the board is quite wide, mark the width at several points and then use a straightedge to draw a line showing the width. Saw to about ⅛ inch of the layout line. Now plane the second edge smooth, straight, and square.
6. Plane the second face. Adjust the marking gage to correct thickness and mark a line from the face surface along the edges and ends. Plane to correct thickness. It is easy to remember the steps: face, edge, end then reverse: end, edge, and face. Steps can be marked on the wood—1, 2, 3; then 3_1, 2_1, 1_1.
7. Some woodworkers like to square

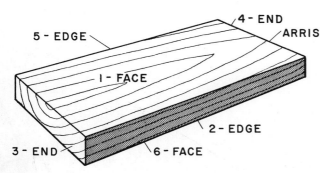

16-1. Steps in squaring up stock.

16-2. Using a cornering tool to remove the sharp edge and to round the corner. (Stanley Tools)

the stock in a different order. They plane the face surface, then the face edge, then the first end, then the second edge, then the second face, and finally the second end.

8. After squaring up stock, use a cornering tool to remove the sharp corners. Fig. 16-2.

QUESTIONS

1. What does S2S mean?
2. Does stock always have to be squared up in order to use it for a project?
3. Is it better to plane the first, or face, edge first before planing the face surface true and smooth?
4. How much material should be allowed for planing end grain?

Unit 17. SHARPENING PLANES AND CHISELS

Planes and chisels cut well only if they are sharp. Dull tools make woodworking difficult and results poor. Tools stay sharp a lot longer if handled correctly. The time you spend putting your tools in condition is rewarded in better work. *Grinding* should be done only when the tool needs a new bevel or when the edge of the cutter is nicked. Otherwise, *honing* is enough.

TOOLS AND MATERIALS

• There are several kinds of power-driven grinders that can be used to sharpen tools. A *slow-speed grinder* is good because there is little danger of overheating the tool blade. Fig. 17-1. On a *fast-speed grinder* you must be careful not to hold the tool blade on the wheel too long. Many grinders have a plane-iron grinding attachment to guide the blade. Fig. 17-2. A *grinder hone* can be used for both grinding and honing cutting edges. Fig. 17-3.

• An *oilstone* is a fine-grained stone used to hone cutting edges. Fig. 17-4. Most oilstones are made from man-made abrasives (grit). The best type

17-1. A slow-speed grinder.

17-2. (a) A fast-speed grinder. (b) A plane-iron grinding attachment. (Stanley Tools)

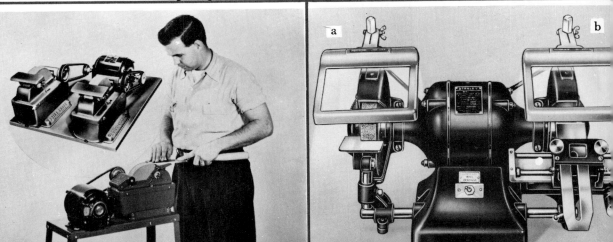

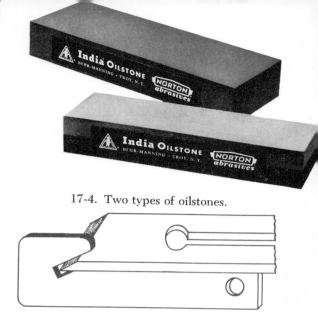

17-4. Two types of oilstones.

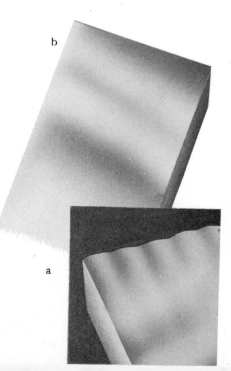

17-5. Checking the angle of a plane-iron blade with a gage.

17-2. (b)

has a medium-coarse stone on one side and a finer abrasive on the other side. A natural stone is preferred by some craftsmen.

• *Oil* is needed (a) to do a faster sharpening job, (b) to get a finer edge, and (c) to keep the stone free of chips. A good mineral oil is recommended.

4. A *bevel-grinding gage* is needed to check the bevel after grinding. Fig. 17-5.

GRINDING A PLANE-IRON BLADE

1. Loosen the screw that holds the plane-iron cap to the plane iron. Separate the two parts.

2. Check the cutting edge of the

17-3. A grinder hone designed for both grinding and honing.

plane iron under a light. If the cutting edge reflects light, it needs sharpening. Fig. 17-6. Are there nicks along the edge? Is the bevel rounded? If so, you must grind and hone both.

3. Hold a try square on the edge of the blade and check to see if the cutting edge is square with the edges. Fig. 17-7.

17-6. The difference between (a) a dull and (b) a sharp plane iron.

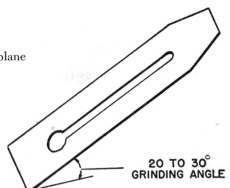

17-7. Checking the cutting edge of a plane
iron with a try square.

4. Grind off the old edge at right
angles to the sides until the nicks are
removed and the edge straightened.
Fig. 17-8.

5. A blade sharpened correctly for
general work will have a straight cutting edge and the corners slightly
rounded off.

**20 TO 30°
GRINDING ANGLE**

17-9. Notice the bevel should be about 2 to
2½ times the thickness of the plane-iron
blade, or at angle of 20 to 30 degrees.

90°

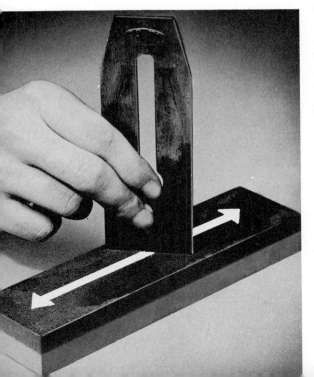

17-10. Using the plane-iron cap as a guide
in grinding.

6. If a grinding attachment is available, fasten the blade in it with the
bevel side down. The bevel should be
2 to 2½ times the thickness of the
blade. This will give a 20- to 30-degree
angle to the cutting edge. Fig. 17-9.

7. If the grinder does not have an
attachment, reverse the plane-iron cap
on the plane iron. Set the cap at right
angles to the plane iron. Check this
with a try square. Then hold the cap
against the front edge of the tool rest.
It may be necessary to move the cap
toward or away from the cutting edge
until the blade just touches the grinding wheel. Fig. 17-10.

8. Move the blade back and forth
across the wheel face. Remove the
blade quite often and dip the edge in

17-8. Making sure that the edge of a plane
iron is straight before grinding or honing.
Here is one way of straightening it.

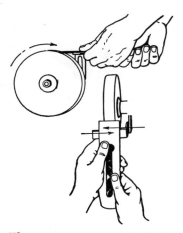

17-11. The correct way to hold the plane iron. Move it back and forth as it is being ground.

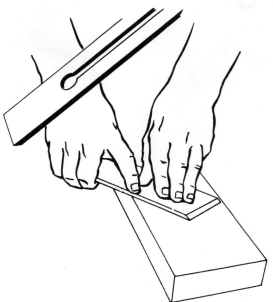

17-13. Removing the burr from the cutting edge by holding the plane-iron flat on the stone.

water to keep it cool. Fig. 17-11. If the blade turns blue, it is overheating. If the edge is burned often, the blade never will hold a cutting edge again.

9. If you're grinding the blade "freehand," grind as close as possible to the same angle after each time the blade is removed. You must get the feel of the grinding. The beginner makes the mistake of holding the blade at different angles, making the bevel very uneven.

10. Continue to grind the blade until a wire edge (a very thin burr) appears.

HONING THE BLADE

1. Apply a few drops of mineral oil to the face of the oilstone.

17-12. Hold the plane iron at the same angle and move it in a figure 8.

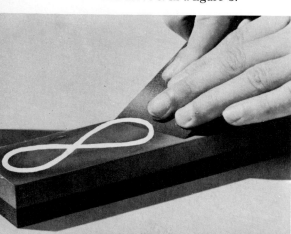

2. Place the blade at a very low angle to the surface, bevel side down. Now raise the end slowly until the blade makes an angle of about 30 to 35 degrees to the stone.

3. To hone the edge, move the blade back and forth in a straight line or in a figure 8. Fig. 17-12. Be sure your hands move parallel to the stone so that the angle stays the same throughout the stroke.

4. Now turn the blade over and place it flat against the stone. Move it back and forth to remove the wire edge. Fig. 17-13. To remove this wire edge, draw the cutting edge across a corner of a soft piece of wood.

5. Test for sharpness in one of the following ways:

    a. Place the cutting edge lightly on your thumbnail. Slide it along. If it sticks and jerks, it is sharp. If it slides easily it is dull.

    b. Try slicing a piece of paper

64

with the blade. It should cut the paper easily.

6. A chisel is sharpened in the same way.

QUESTIONS

1. Why should planes and chisels be kept sharp?

2. Name three kinds of grinders.

3. What kind of oilstone is best for honing the edges?

4. What should you check when you look at the cutting edge of a plane iron?

5. At about what angle should the bevel be on a plane iron?

6. Why should the plane iron be kept cool when grinding it?

7. Describe the way to hone a plane.

8. There are two methods of testing the sharpness of a plane iron. Which is the safest?

Unit 18. CUTTING CURVES AND INSIDE OPENINGS

Many cutout designs and projects have curved edges, very sharp corners, or angles that must be cut with a thin saw blade. Inside openings also must be cut with a narrow blade.

TOOLS

• The *coping saw* has a U-shaped frame and a handle which hold a replaceable blade. The blade can be adjusted to any angle to the frame. Fig. 18-1.

• The *compass saw* has a tapered blade that fits into a handle. It is really a fine-tooth crosscut saw. Sometimes several sizes of blades are furnished with the same handle. Fig. 18-2. It is used to cut curves and inside openings.

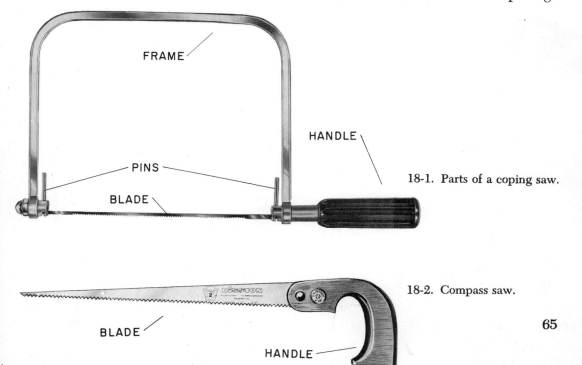

FRAME

PINS

BLADE

HANDLE

18-1. Parts of a coping saw.

18-2. Compass saw.

BLADE

HANDLE

65

• A *keyhole saw* is much like a compass saw except that it is smaller and has a shorter blade.

• A *saw bracket, or jack,* is a wooden support used with a coping saw. One type is a rectangular piece of wood with a V cut out of the end. This is clamped to the top of the table. The other type is clamped in a vise so you can stand up to do the cutting.

• *Coping-saw blades* are made in different widths with teeth similar to a rip saw. Blades with ten to fifteen teeth to the inch are used for wood while those with twenty and thirty-two teeth are for cutting metal. Another type of blade has spiral-shaped teeth that will saw up or down, right or left, or in circles.

USING A COPING SAW WITH THE WORK HELD IN THE VISE

1. Fasten the work in the vise with the start of the layout line just above the vise jaws. Move the work away from the top of the vise a little at a time as the cutting proceeds. If the sawing is done too far away from the vise, the work vibrates and makes the cutting difficult.

2. Install a blade in the frame with the teeth pointing *away from the handle.* Hold the saw in both hands as shown in Fig. 18-3. Cut just outside the layout line, using even strokes. Apply a little pressure as you push forward. Release the pressure as you pull back.

3. Guide the saw frame so that the saw follows the line. At sharp curves, move the saw back and forth as you slowly turn the frame without applying much pressure. *Do not twist the saw,* as this will break the blade.

5. The blade can be turned at any angle to the frame. Make sure both pins

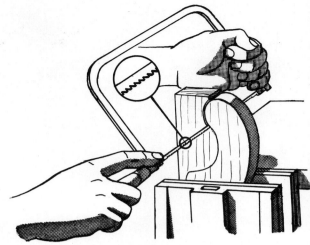

18-3. Sawing a curve with the work held in a vise. The teeth must be pointed away from the handle.

are turned the same amount. For example, to make a long cut, adjust the blade at a right angle to the frame.

USING A COPING SAW WITH THE WORK HELD OVER A SAW JACK OR BRACKET

1. Clamp the bracket to the bench or in the vise.

2. Fasten a blade in the frame with the teeth pointing *toward the handle.* The cutting is done on the down stroke.

3. Hold the work firmly on the bracket, with the area to be cut near the bottom of the V.

18-4. (a) Using a coping saw with the work held over a saw bracket or jack.

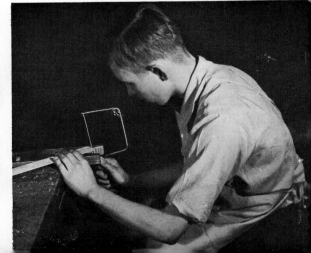

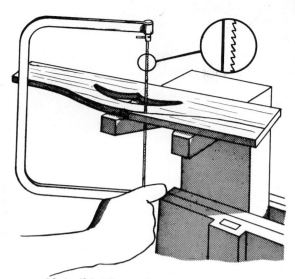

18-4. (b) The teeth must be pointed toward the handle.

4. Draw down on the saw to cut. Move the work so the cutting is always near the bottom of the V. Fig. 18-4.

5. For inside cutting, drill or bore a hole in the waste stock. Remove the blade from the frame. Then slip the blade through the hole and fasten it in the frame again. Cut up to and around

18-5. Sawing a curve using a compass saw.

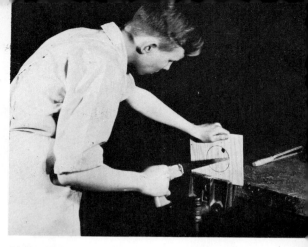

18-6. Cutting an inside curve with the compass saw. Note that a hole has been bored in the waste stock close to the layout line.

the design. Then remove the blade.

USING A COMPASS SAW

• This saw is best for sawing gentle curves in heavy stock.

• For outside curves, use short strokes. Fig. 18-5. Twist the handle slightly to follow the curve. Do not force the saw, as it may bend or buckle.

• For inside curves, bore a hole in the waste stock to start the cutting. Fig. 18-6. Sometimes a hole is part of the design. Start the saw, using short strokes. Work slowly. For very small openings, use the *keyhole saw,* which is like a miniature compass saw.

QUESTIONS

1. List three kinds of saws for sawing curves and irregular shapes.

2. In using a coping saw with the work held in a vise, how should the blade be installed in the frame?

3. Why must the work be held securely when using a coping saw?

4. How should the blade be placed in a coping saw when cutting with the work held over a saw bracket?

5. What must you do before you can cut an inside opening?

6. What is the difference between a keyhole saw and a compass saw?

Three angle surfaces cut in the same way are the chamfer, bevel, and taper. A *chamfer* is a slanted surface made by cutting off an edge, end, or corner. The chamfered edge is cut only part way

19-1. (a) A chamfer. (b) A bevel. (c) A taper.

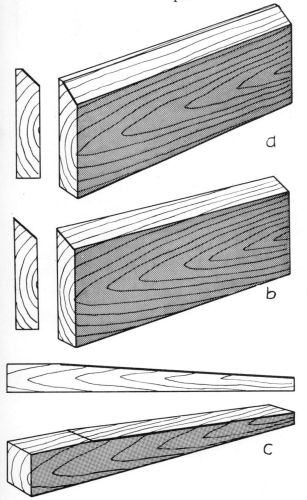

down the edge, usually at an angle of 45 degrees. Fig. 19-1 (a). A chamfer is cut in order to remove the sharp edge and improve appearance. A *bevel* is a sloping edge. Fig. 19-1 (b). It is used, for example, to fit two pieces together to form a V shape. A *taper* is a cut that becomes gradually smaller toward one end. Fig. 19-1 (c). For example, tent pegs and the legs of tables, chairs, and stools are often tapered. Sometimes all four sides of a leg are tapered, or only the two inside sides may be tapered.

TOOLS

• The *sliding T bevel* is used to lay out and check "odd" angles—other than 45 or 90 degrees. Fig. 19-2. It consists of a handle with an adjustable blade. A clamping screw at one end of the handle locks the blade. To set a bevel, use a protractor or carpenter's square. A metal *protractor* is used if you must set the bevel at an odd angle, such as 62 degrees. Fig. 19-3. To set a sliding T bevel to a 45-degree angle, hold the blade of the bevel across the corner

19-2. Parts of a sliding T bevel. (Stanley Tools)

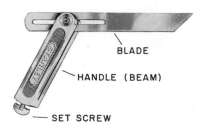

BLADE

HANDLE (BEAM)

SET SCREW

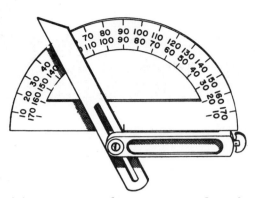

19-3. Using a metal protractor to adjust the sliding T bevel.

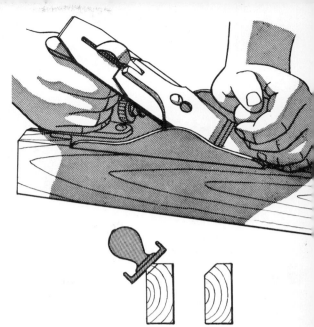

of a carpenter's square until there is equal distance on the body and tongue. To set a 30- or 60-degree angle, set the blade to 3 inches on the tongue and 5 3/16 inches on the body. Fig. 19-4.
• Plane, pencil, rule and try square.

CUTTING A CHAMFER

1. Decide on the amount of the chamfer. For example, on ¾-inch stock, the chamfer usually is made 3/16 to ¼ inch.

19-4. Setting the blade to 3 inches on the tongue and 5 3/16 inches on the blade of the carpenter's square. This setting gives angles of 30 and 60 degrees.

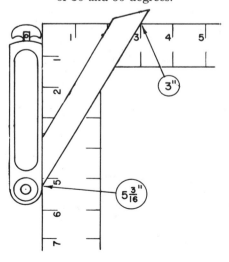

19-5. Planing a chamfer. See how the plane is held at an angle of about 45 degrees.

2. Lay out the lines for all chamfers with a pencil. *Never use a marking gage.* The spur of the marking gage will cut a groove that never comes out.

3. Clamp the work in a vise with the chamfer side toward you and somewhat above the top of the vise.

4. Tilt the plane at about a 45-degree angle and begin to plane. Fig. 19-5. You may guide the plane by curling the fingers of your left hand under the bottom of the plane. Make the movements of the plane even and long.

5. After you have planed part way, check the chamfer. Fig. 19-6. Is there

19-6. Checking a chamfer to make sure it is even.

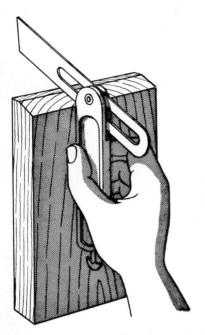

19-7. Using a sliding T bevel to check a chamfer or bevel.

about an equal amount to be removed to bring it to the layout lines? If not, you might have to tilt the plane more in the direction where the most stock must be removed. You can check the chamfer with a sliding T bevel. Fig. 19-7.

6. Always plane the chamfer *with the grain* (along the edges first).

7. To plane end grain, clamp the work rather high in a vise. Make a shearing cut to plane the chamfer. Fig. 19-8. This is done by holding the plane at an angle as well as at a tilt.

8. For small work a block plane is a good tool to use.

CUTTING A BEVEL

1. Determine the angle of the bevel and adjust the sliding T bevel.

2. Mark a line across the ends of the stock to show the bevel angle. Then draw a line across the second surface of the board as a guide.

3. Plane the bevel as you did a chamfer. Check frequently with the T bevel to be sure you are cutting it at the correct angle.

CUTTING A TAPER

1. Mark a line around the leg to show how far the taper will go.

2. If the leg is to be tapered on all four sides, first mark the two opposite sides on one end to show the amount of the taper. Draw lines along the legs to show the stock to be removed. If the leg is tapered only on two sides, mark the taper on one side only.

3. If it is a rather sharp taper, saw away some of the waste stock. Planing is usually enough, however.

4. Clamp the work in a vise with the taper line parallel to the top.

5. Start planing near the end of the leg. Each cut will be a little longer until you have reached the taper line.

6. After you have planed both sides (or one side if only two are to be tapered), lay out and cut the taper on the other two sides.

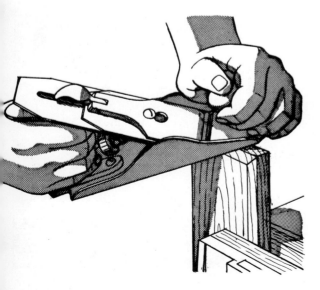

19-8. Planing an end grain chamfer using a shearing cut.

1. Describe a chamfer.
2. How is a bevel different from a chamfer?
3. What is a taper?
4. What is the size of a chamfer on ¾-inch stock?

5. Why should a marking gage never be used in laying out a chamfer?
6. How could you hold a plane in planing a chamfer?
7. What tool do you need to lay out a bevel?
8. Where is a taper most commonly used?

Unit 20. CUTTING WITH CHISELS

A *chisel* is a strong, steel cutting tool with a sharp bevel edge at one end. Chisels are used to shape and fit parts. It is important to know how to choose a sharp chisel and how to handle it correctly. It is easy to cut yourself because the chisel has a sharp, exposed blade. Keep your fingers clear of the cutting edge while working.

TOOLS

• *Chisels* are two types: the *tang* (also called *shank*) and the *socket*. Fig. 20-1. The tang chisel has a short point, or tang, that extends into the wood handle. Present-day tang chisels have the blade and tang in one piece. The tang

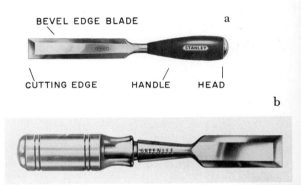

20-1. (a) A tang chisel. The tang, or shank, extends all the way through the handle and is attached to a steel head. (Stanley Tools) (b) A socket chisel. The handle fits into the socket (the cup-shaped part of the blade).

20 A1. Using a chisel. Remember the six basic machines, page 41. The cutting edge of a chisel is half a *wedge*. The sharper the wedge the better the machine. That is why sharp cutting tools are so important. The handle is a *lever*. The upper side of blade acts as an *inclined plane* to allow the chip to move more easily up the machine.

extends through the handle to a metal cap. The socket chisel has a socket (cup shape) at the end of the blade into which the handle fits. Chisel size is shown by blade widths, ranging from ⅛ to 1 inch, by ⅛ths and from 1 inch to 2 inches, by ¼ths. The most com-

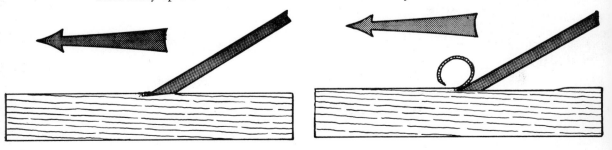

20-2. A mallet.

mon sizes are ¼, ½, ¾, 1, 1¼, and 1½ inch.

• A *mallet* is a short-handled hammer with a large head made of wood, rawhide, or plastic. It is used to strike a chisel for heavy cutting. Fig. 20-2.

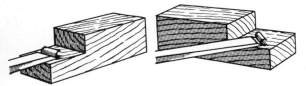

20-3. Always cut with the grain—as at right. Avoid cutting against the grain (left).

HORIZONTAL CUTTING ACROSS GRAIN

1. Select a chisel. Make sure it is sharp and free of nicks.
2. Clamp the work in a vise or

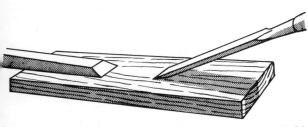

20-4. For light chiseling (trimming), hold the beveled side up. For heavier cutting, place the bevel side down.

20-5. Making rough cuts with the bevel side down. Strike the chisel with a mallet.

20-6. Making a long, horizontal cut with the bevel side down.

fasten it to the top of the bench. Cut across grain or with the grain, never against it. Fig. 20-3.

3. To remove large amounts of wood, turn the chisel with the *bevel side down.* Fig. 20-4.

4. Hold the chisel in your left hand and strike it with a mallet. Cut from both sides towards the center. Fig. 20-5. Cutting from one side will chip out the opposite edge.

5. When the cutting is within about ⅛ inch of the layout line, continue the cutting by hand.

6. For light trimming, turn the chisel with the *bevel up.* Guide the blade by pressing your left hand against the edge of the wood. Work at a slight angle to the grain.

7. Apply pressure with your right hand, cutting a little at a time. Sometimes you must swing the handle from side to side to do the cutting.

8. Be sure to hold the flat side parallel to the work but at an angle to the grain.

HORIZONTAL CUTTING WITH THE GRAIN

1. Clamp the work in a vise so you can cut with the grain.

2. For heavy cutting, hold the chisel with the bevel side down. For light paring cuts, hold the chisel with the bevel side up.

3. Grasp the blade in your left hand and the handle in your right hand. Reverse if lefthanded. Fig. 20-6.

4. Press forward as you push the cutting edge into the wood.

5. Guide the chisel so the cut isn't too deep.

6. Sometimes it is better to move the handle back and forth in a short arc as you push.

VERTICAL CUTTING ACROSS GRAIN

1. Place the work over a bench hook or scrap stock.

2. Hold the chisel with the flat side against the wood.

3. Rest one hand on the wood to guide the chisel and use your other hand to apply pressure. Fig. 20-7.

4. Take a light cut. Apply pressure and move the handle in an arc from an angle to a vertical position. This makes a shearing cut.

CUTTING A CONVEX (CURVED-OUT) SURFACE

1. Clamp the work in a vise so the cutting can be done with the grain (towards the end grain).

2. Hold the chisel with the flat side down. Fig. 20-8.

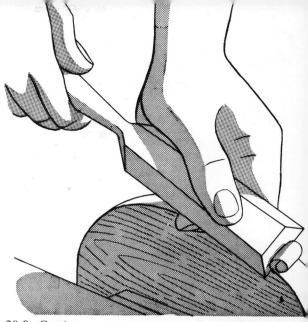

20-8. Cutting a convex curve. Raise the handle a little at a time to follow the curve.

20-9. Cutting a concave curve. Always cut from the edge toward the end grain.

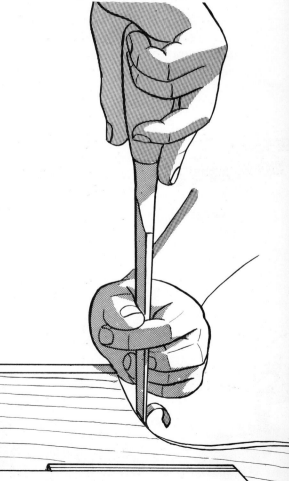

20-7. Cutting vertically across the grain. Notice how the left hand guides the chisel as the right hand applies pressure.

3. Guide the chisel with one hand and press forward with the other. Move the handle in an arc that is the same as the convex surface.

CUTTING A CONCAVE (CURVED-IN) SURFACE

1. Hold the chisel with the bevel side down. Cut with the grain. Fig. 20-9.

2. Move the handle toward you as you press forward.

QUESTIONS

1. Name the parts of a chisel.
2. Describe two types of chisels.
3. What is a mallet? How does it differ from a hammer?
4. How should you hold a chisel when doing horizontal cutting across grain?
5. Why should work be placed on a bench hook or scrap stock when doing vertical cutting?
6. What is meant by convex? Concave?
7. In which direction should you cut when chiseling a convex surface?

Unit 21. SHAPING WITH GOUGES, CARVING TOOLS, AND KNIVES

To shape such things as the inside of a fruit tray, model-boat hull, or carved animal figure, Fig. 21-1, you need sharp gouges and carving tools. Tools are made in many different shapes and sizes to do all kinds of internal shaping, carving, and whittling.

21-1. This attractive tray is the kind of project that can be made by shaping the wood with gouges.

TOOLS

• A *gouge* is a chisel with a curved blade. It is used to cut grooves and holes and to shape openings in wood. Gouges come in common blade sizes from ⅛ inch to 2 inches. The size is measured between corners. The blade may be sharpened or ground on the *inside* or the *outside*. The outside-ground gouge is the most common. The inside gouge is needed for cutting a curve that runs vertically. Fig. 21-2, 3.

• A *carving-tool set* is a group of gouge tools each with a different-shaped blade. These are used for detailed carving and shaping. Fig. 21-4.

• A *carving set* has different-shaped

21-3. Notice the difference in shape between an inside and an outside gouge.

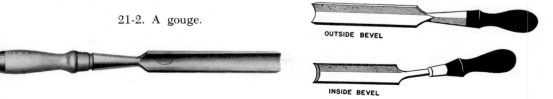

OUTSIDE BEVEL

INSIDE BEVEL

21-2. A gouge.

74

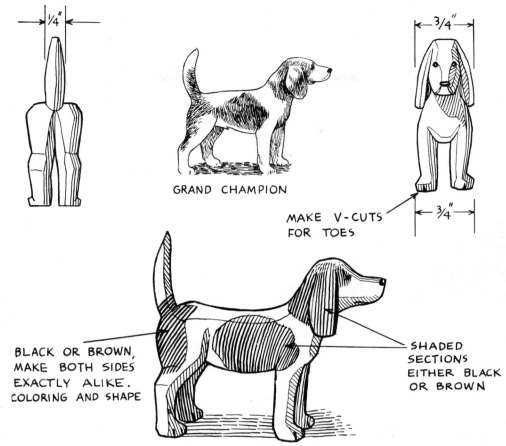

GRAND CHAMPION

MAKE V-CUTS
FOR TOES

BLACK OR BROWN,
MAKE BOTH SIDES
EXACTLY ALIKE.
COLORING AND SHAPE

SHADED
SECTIONS
EITHER BLACK
OR BROWN

A project made by whittling.

replaceable blades for model making, hand carving, and whittling. Fig. 21-5.
• A *sloyd knife*.

21-4. A carving-tool set.

USING A GOUGE

1. Mark the area to be removed by the gouge.

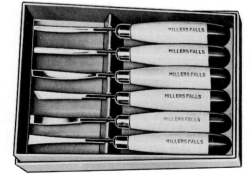

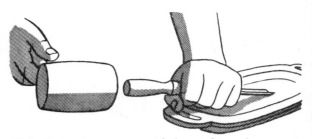

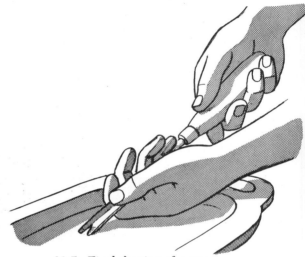

21-6. Removing waste stock by striking the chisel with the mallet.

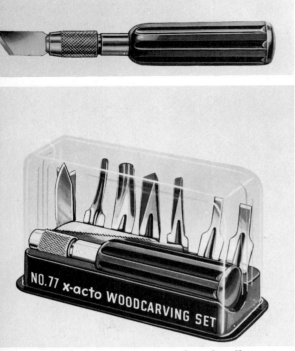

21-5. A carving set with a handle and replaceable blade.

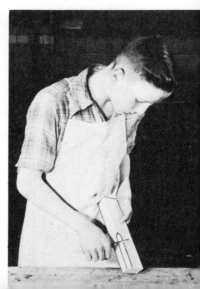

21-7. Final shaping of a tray.

2. Fasten the work in a vise or clamp it to the bench top with a hand clamp.

3. Rest the blade of the gouge in your left hand and the handle in your right.

4. Start near the center of the waste area. Hold the gouge at an angle of about 30 degrees and make long strokes with the grain. Guide the blade with your left hand.

5. Force the gouge into the wood only enough to remove a long, thin shaving. To cut end grain, move the cutting edge in a circular motion.

6. To remove a great amount of waste stock, strike the end of the gouge with a mallet to drive the blade into the wood. Fig. 21-6.

7. As you approach the layout line, take thin shavings in all directions from the layout line toward the center. Fig. 21-7.

8. Sand the surface to remove small irregularities.

USING CARVING TOOLS

• Carving tools are used in the same

21-8. A safe way to use a knife.

76

When pulling the knife, keep your thumb below and out of the way of the cutting edge.

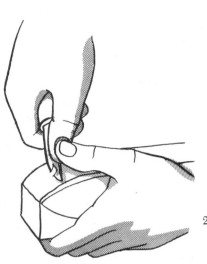

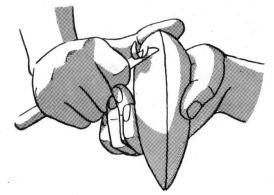

21-9. Two methods of whittling: Pull and push.

general manner as gouges.
• Roughly shape the work with a gouge and the large blades of the carving tools.
• For detail work, use the special shaped tools.

WOOD CARVING OR WHITTLING

1. Lay out the general shape of the model on stock of the correct size.
2. Cut out the rough shape on a jig saw and/or a coping saw.
3. Using a sharp knife, start the whittling in the corners or where the detail is greatest. Cut with the grain.
4. Always cut away from yourself if possible. Fig. 21-8. Sometimes you'll need to cut toward yourself. At all times be especially careful that the knife doesn't slip. Fig. 21-9.
5. Shape both sides the same, cutting a little at a time.

QUESTIONS

1. What is a gouge?
2. What are the uses of carving tools?
3. Name two types of gouges.
4. Describe the way to use a gouge for removing a large amount of material.
5. When should a mallet be used with a gouge?
6. Name at least two safety rules for doing wood carving or whittling.

Unit 22. SHAPING WITH A SPOKESHAVE OR DRAWKNIFE

To form irregular shaped objects, such as archery bows, tool handles, paddles, model-boat hulls, or carved figures, two good tools are the spokeshave and drawknife. Both have sharp cutting edges. The spokeshave is much safer than the drawknife because the blade is enclosed in a frame.

TOOLS

• The *spokeshave* is a small cutting tool much like a simple plane. It has a handle at either side. It was named this because it was originally used to shape the spokes of wagon wheels. It has a frame about 10 to 12 inches long, a blade, and a cap. The blade can be

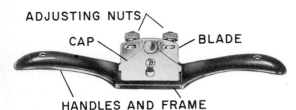

ADJUSTING NUTS

CAP — — BLADE

HANDLES AND FRAME

22-1. Parts of a spokeshave. (Stanley Tools)

adjusted with two small thumb nuts. It is a very safe tool to use. Fig. 22-1.

• The *drawknife* (drawing knife) is an open, beveled blade with a handle at either side. It is used to remove a lot of stock from a wood surface. It has this name because it actually is a knife you draw toward yourself. *The exposed blade can be very dangerous.* Usually about 8 or 10 inches long, the size is determined by the length of the blade. Fig. 22-2.

USING A SPOKESHAVE

1. Adjust the blade (cutter) until it can just be seen through the mouth of the frame. Don't have it exposed too far. If you do, the tool will chatter (jump away) as you use it and make small ridges in the wood.

2. Fasten the work in a vise so you can push or pull the tool across the surface. Work with the grain. Fig. 22-3.

3. To push the spokeshave, grasp the handles in either hand with your thumbs just behind the blade on either side of the frame.

4. Hold the bottom of the frame firmly against the wood and push evenly. Try it a few times. You should produce a long, thin shaving. Make the tool follow the shape of the work.

5. To pull the tool, draw it toward you in long, even strokes.

22-2. Parts of a drawknife.

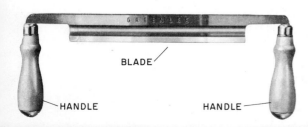

BLADE

HANDLE   HANDLE

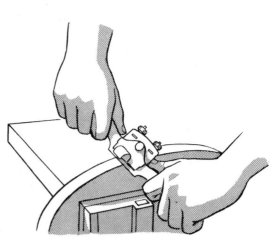

22-3. Pushing the spokeshave to shape a curved edge. Your thumbs are placed on either side near the blade.

USING A DRAWKNIFE

1. The drawknife must be *very sharp*. A dull tool is especially dangerous.

2. Clamp the work securely in a vise so it will be easy to draw the tool across the wood. *Be careful* as you draw or pull it, so it doesn't slip and cause an injury. Fig. 22-4.

3. Hold the tool with the bevel side down. Cut with the grain whenever possible. If you aren't careful, the tool will dig in and split the wood rather than shape it.

4. The depth of cut will be deter-

22-4. Stand far enough away from the tool to be well protected.

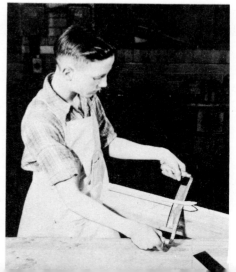

mined by the angle at which you hold the blade. Fig. 22-5. Twist the wrists to control this angle.

QUESTIONS

1. What would be a good tool for forming an archery bow?
2. Why is the spokeshave safer than the drawknife?
3. Why is a spokeshave like a simple plane?
4. Why must you be careful in using a drawknife?
5. How should the blade of a spokeshave be adjusted?
6. In what directions can you work the spokeshave?
7. In which direction should the bevel side be when using a drawknife?

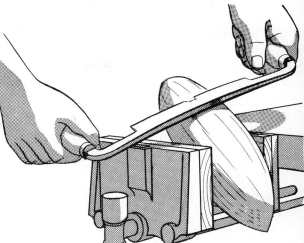

22-5. Shaping a boat hull with the drawknife.

Unit 23. SHAPING WITH FILES, RASPS, AND FORMING TOOLS

The good woodworker uses files, rasps, and forming tools only when saws or other edge-cutting tools won't do the job as well. You'll find many uses for these tools for repair jobs, for fitting, and for forming odd-shaped parts.

TOOLS

• There are many shapes of files but the most common ones for woodworking are *half-round cabinet* and *flat wood files* in lengths of 8, 10 or 12 inches, Fig. 23-1. Wood files usually

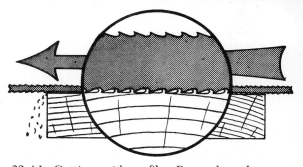

23-A1. Cutting with a file. Remember the six basic machines, page 41. A file or rasp is made up of many small *wedges*. The force you apply to the file handle is divided among the many teeth so that there is a smaller force at each wedge to do the cutting.

23-1. Parts of a flat wood file.

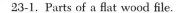

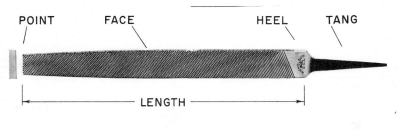

POINT   FACE   HEEL   TANG

LENGTH

23-2. A flat and half-round rasp.

have double-cut teeth. That is, there are two rows of teeth cut diagonally across the face. The file is not as rough as the wood rasp.

• The *rasp* is a tool with individual cutting teeth. Fig. 23-2. It removes material faster than a file but leaves a rougher surface.

• A *file cleaner,* or *file card,* is needed to keep the teeth of the file or rasp clean and free from wood, resin, or finishing materials. See Fig. 23-6.

• The *surform* is a forming tool with a hardened and tempered tool-steel cutting blade. Fig. 23-3. The blade has

45-degree cutting edges with many small openings that easily cut wood, plastic, or soft metals. The teeth of this tool never become clogged. The replaceable blade fits into a holder.

USING A FILE OR RASP

1. Files or rasps are never to be used without handles. *The tang can puncture your hand* and cause a serious injury. Always fit a handle to the tool before using it. Fig. 23-4.

2. Clamp the work in a vise.

3. Select the finest tool possible. A tool too coarse will splinter the wood.

4. Hold the handle of the tool in

23-3. Surform tool. (a) File type. (b) Plane type.

23-4. Always fit a handle over the tang of the file or rasp.

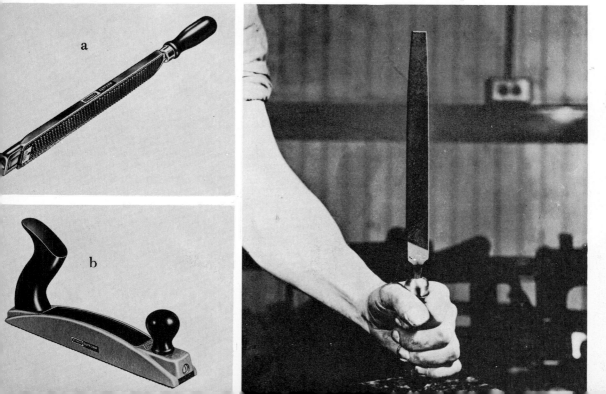

23-5. Using a wood rasp to shape wood.

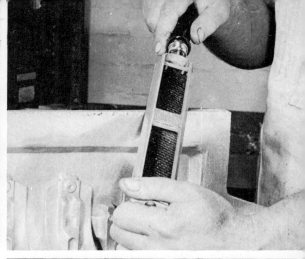

your right hand and the point in your left.

5. Apply moderate (a medium amount of) pressure on the forward stroke. Fig. 23-5. Make a shearing cut at a slight angle. Lift the file slightly on the return stroke.

6. To shape a curved edge, use the round side of the tool. Twist the tool slightly as you push.

7. Always keep the teeth clean with the file card or cleaner. Fig. 23-6.

8. A piece of sandpaper of the correct grade can be wrapped around the file to smooth the surface or edge after a file or rasp has been used. A round file may be used to shape an inside opening.

Using a Surform Tool

• Use this tool as you would a rasp.
• To get best results, apply light, even pressure against the wood. Fig. 23-7.

23-6. Cleaning a file.

23-7. Shaping a surface with a surform tool:
(a) Using the file type. (b) Using the plane type. (Stanley Tools)

The surform produces a smooth, even surface.
• As a repair tool it is excellent to smooth an edge or end that has been chipped or splintered. The surform is ideal for shaping a gun stock, canoe paddle, wooden handle for a tool, or other odd-shaped piece.

Questions

1. Name the common kinds of files used in woodworking.

2. How does a rasp differ from a file?

3. What is a surform tool?

4. What is the first thing you should do when you buy or take out a new file or rasp?

5. How do you shape a curve or edge with a file?

6. What is used to keep the teeth of the file clean?

7. Describe the way a surform tool operates.

Unit 24. DRILLING HOLES

Small holes are needed to install screws, nails, and small bolts. Small holes are also part of the construction of many projects. The holes in a cribbage board are a good example. These holes are *drilled* with twist drills.

TOOLS

• *Twist drills* come in fractional-sized sets from 1/64 to 1/2 inch, in steps of 1/64th inch. Fig. 24-1. These drills can be used for both metal and wood. Sizes ¼ inch and smaller can be held in a *hand drill*. Larger sizes can be used in a *breast drill* or drill press. See Unit 27.

24-A1. Drilling a hole. Remember the six basic machines, page 41. A drill or auger bit is a combination of several simple machines. The cutting edge is a wedge and the body is a *screw*. The brace you use on an auger bit is a good example of a *wheel and axle*. The brace handle is like one spoke of a *wheel*.

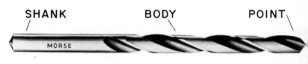

SHANK   BODY   POINT

MORSE

24-1. Parts of a twist drill. The size is stamped on the shank.

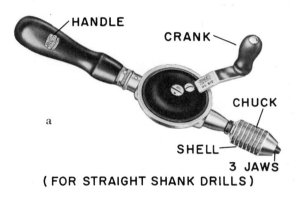

HANDLE

CRANK

CHUCK

a

SHELL

3 JAWS

(FOR STRAIGHT SHANK DRILLS)

24-2. (a) Parts of a hand drill. (b) Breast drill. (Stanley Tools)

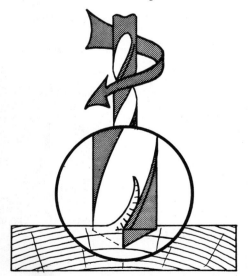

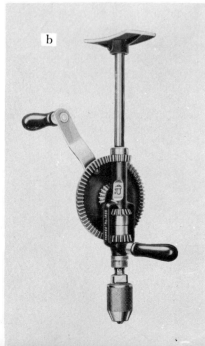

b

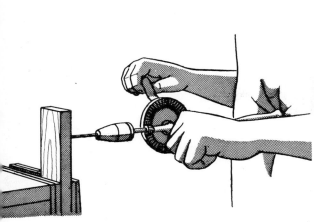

24-3. Drilling a hole in a horizontal position with the breast drill.

• The parts of a *hand drill* are shown in Fig. 24-2 (a). Most hand drills are made to hold drills up to ¼ inch in diameter. *Breast drills* are usually made to hold drills up to ½ inch in diameter. Fig. 24-2 (b).

DRILLING

1. Mark the locations for the holes with a scratch awl or sharp-pointed nail. The drill starts a lot easier when the location is punched.

2. Fasten the work in a vise so you can drill either vertically (up and down) or horizontally. Fig. 24-3.

3. Grasp the shell of the chuck in your left hand and turn the crank counterclockwise (opposite of clockwise) until the shank of the drill will slip in. Then turn the crank in the other direction to tighten. Make sure

24-4. A depth gage made from a piece of dowel rod covering a part of the drill like a sleeve. Cut the piece until the drill sticks out the right amount. See Unit 31.

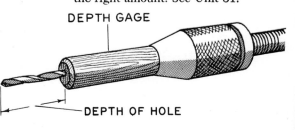

DEPTH GAGE

DEPTH OF HOLE

24-5. Drilling is sometimes needed when nails must be placed very close to the edge. Use a drill that is slightly smaller in diameter than the nail.

the drill is in the chuck straight, so it doesn't wobble.

4. If holes of a certain depth are needed (holes for screws, for example), make a *depth gage* from a piece of scrap wood. Fig. 24-4.

5. Place the point of the drill where you want the hole and turn the crank evenly as you apply light pressure to the handle. Press straight down or

24-6. Drilling holes with an electric hand drill.

ahead. *Be careful not to tip the hand drill after it is started.* This will break the drill. Fig. 24-5.

6. Continue to turn the handle in the same direction as you pull the drill out of the hole.

7. Always return the drill to the correct holder.

USING AN ELECTRIC HAND DRILL. A small electric hand drill is very useful for drilling small holes. The size shown in Fig. 24-6 will hold any drill ¼ inch or smaller.

1. Use a chuck key to open the chuck. Insert the twist drill and then tighten the chuck. Make sure the drill runs straight. Remove the chuck key immediately.

2. Hold the point of the drill over the place you want the hole.

3. Guide the drill with one hand and apply pressure with the other. The drill cuts a hole quickly so be careful that it doesn't go in too far. If the revolving chuck touches the wood surface it will mar it.

4. It is easy to break small drills in an electric hand drill. Hold the drill steady.

QUESTIONS
1. Why is drilling small holes necessary?
2. Describe the parts of a hand drill.
3. Tell how to fasten a twist drill in a hand drill.
4. How can you tell the size of a small electric drill?

Unit 25. BORING HOLES

Boring is cutting a hole in wood with a tool called a *bit*. Holes ¼ inch or larger are *bored*. Holes ¼ inch or smaller are *drilled*. Boring is the first step in making a rectangular-shaped opening.

TOOLS

• A *brace* holds the auger bit when the holes are bored. Fig. 25-1. The two most common braces are the *plain,* or *common,* and the *ratchet.* The auger bit goes into the wood as you turn the handle. The plain brace is used when you can make a full swing of the handle. If you have the problem of boring

25-1. Parts of a brace. (Stanley Tools)

25-2. (a) A single-twist auger bit. (b) Parts of a double-twist auger bit. (Stanley Tools)

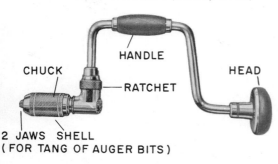

HANDLE
CHUCK
HEAD
RATCHET
2 JAWS SHELL
(FOR TANG OF AUGER BITS)

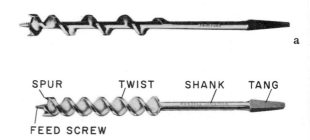

a

SPUR   TWIST   SHANK   TANG

FEED SCREW

b

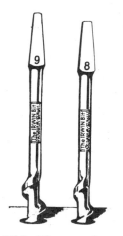

25-3. The number stamped on the tang shows the size of the auger bit. Left: 9/16 inch. Right: 1/2 or 8/16 inch.

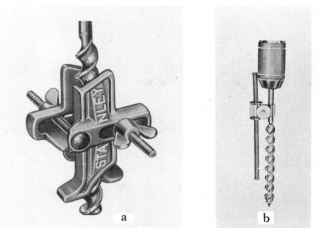

25-4. Bit or depth gages: (a) Solid type. (b) Spring type. (Stanley Tools)

in a corner or in close quarters, you need a *ratchet brace*. To use it, turn the ratchet control to the right (clockwise). The brace can then turn the bit to the right. The ratchet slips when the brace is rotated to the left. In this way a half turn or less at a time will bore the hole. If the ratchet is turned to the left, the bit can be rotated out of the hole. To use the ratchet brace as a regular brace, set the ratchet in the center position.

• The *auger bit* is the most common cutting tool. Fig. 25-2. It ranges in size from ¼ inch (No. 4) to 1 inch (No. 16), by sixteenths. A number stamped on the shank of the *bit* tells the size in sixteenths. For example, size 8 is 8/16 or ½ inch, while a 9 bores a 9/16-inch hole. Fig. 25-3. The screw on the end of the bit pulls the bit into the wood.
• A *depth gage (bit gage)* is a device that is attached to the auger bit to limit the depth of the hole. A *homemade gage* can be made by boring a hole through a piece of wood until the correct bit length is exposed. See Fig. 24-4. Two commercial bit gages are shown in Fig. 25-4.

HORIZONTAL (FLAT OR LEVEL) BORING

1. Choose the correct size bit. For example, if the drawing calls for a ¾-inch hole, choose a No. 12 bit.
2. Insert the bit in the brace. Grasp the shell firmly in one hand. Rotate the handle to the left until the jaws are open enough to receive the shank. Then turn the handle to the right to tighten the bit. Fig. 25-5.
3. Mark the location of the hole with two intersection lines. Center punch with a scratch awl or point of a nail.
4. Fasten the work in a vise with the center-punch mark near the top or side of the vise jaw.

25-5. Inserting the shank well into the two jaws. The corners should be in the V grooves of the jaws.

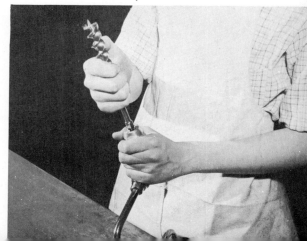

25-6. Horizontal boring bit. Remember to keep the auger bit at right angles with the work.

5. Guide the bit with your left hand until the screw point is exactly on the punch mark. Hold the head in your left hand braced against your stomach. Grasp the handle in your right hand. If lefthanded, reverse these instructions.

6. Now you should ask a friend to help you "sight" the tool so the hole will be square with the wood surface. You sight it right and left. Fig. 25-6. Have your friend sight it up and down.

7. Turn the handle steadily. In softwood, little pressure is needed because the screw easily draws the point into the wood. For hardwood, press a little harder on the head.

8. Watch carefully for the feed screw to start coming out the opposite side. Stop. Turn the handle in the opposite direction to remove the bit. If you don't stop, the wood will split out. Fig. 25-7.

9. Turn the work around and finish the hole by boring from the other side.

10. You can bore the hole completely through from one side if you place a piece of scrap stock back of your work.

VERTICAL BORING

1. Locate the hole. Clamp the work with the surface up.

2. Start the auger bit by turning it clockwise. Fig. 25-8.

3. Use a square, or a block of wood, as shown in Fig. 25-9, to make sure the bit enters the wood straight.

4. Continue the boring as described above.

STOP BORING, OR BORING TO DEPTH

1. Attach a depth or bit gage to the

25-7. (a) This shows what happens when you continue to bore from one side. (b) Boring from one side until the screw appears and then reversing the auger bit. (c) Using a piece of scrap stock to bore directly through the work.

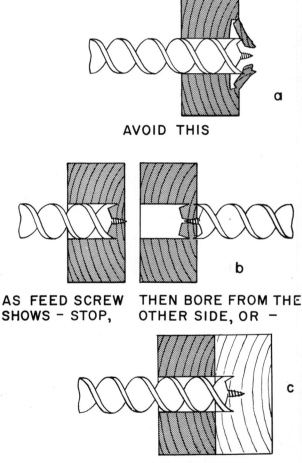

AVOID THIS

AS FEED SCREW SHOWS – STOP,

THEN BORE FROM THE OTHER SIDE, OR –

USE SCRAP WOOD

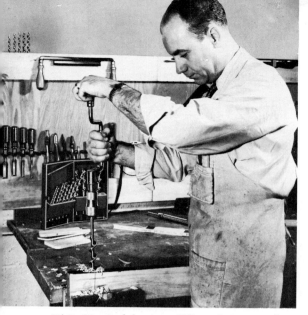

25-8. Vertical boring. When doing machine work, you would remove all jewelry.

bit, with the right length of the cutting tool showing.

2. Bore the hole until the gage touches the surface.

USING AN EXPANSION BIT. An *expansion* (expansive) *bit* is used to bore a hole larger than 1 inch. Most expansion bits have two cutters, each a different size, so a wide range of hole sizes can be bored. Fig. 25-10.

25-9. Checking to make sure the auger bit is square with the work.

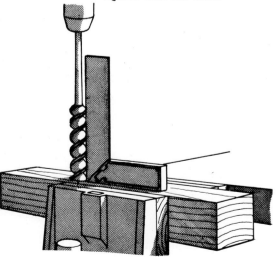

1. Choose a cutter of the correct size and slip it into the bit. Adjust the cutter until the distance from the *spur* to the cutter edge equals the *radius* of the hole. Fig. 25-11. A scale on the cutter helps set it. This scale shows the hole diameter. On some types there is an adjusting screw for moving the cutter. Lock the cutter by tightening the lock screw.

2. Fasten the bit in a brace.

3. Clamp a piece of scrap stock in the vise or to the bench top and make a test cut. Is the hole size correct?

4. Mark the location of the hole.

5. *It is very important to have the work held tightly.* Fig. 25-12. Since the bit has only one cutter, it will twist the work if it isn't clamped. It's a good idea to put a piece of scrap stock behind the work. Thin wood tends to crack or split.

6. As you rotate the tool, use just enough pressure to make it cut.

7. When the spur shows through, reverse the work and cut from the other side.

8. Rock the bit from side to side to cut through the last of the hole.

USING A FOERSTNER BIT. A *Foerstner bit* can be used when an auger bit will not work well. Fig. 25-13. Some examples are (a) boring a shallow hole that has a flat bottom (Fig. 25-14), (b) boring a hole in thin stock near the

25-10. Parts of an expansion bit. (Stanley Tools)

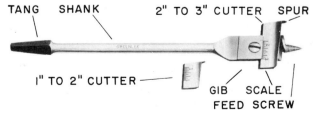

TANG   SHANK   2" TO 3" CUTTER   SPUR

I" TO 2" CUTTER —   GIB   SCALE
                      FEED SCREW

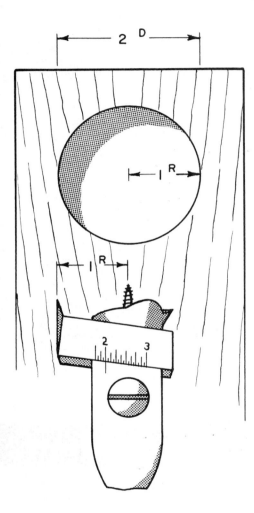

25-11. Notice that the expansion bit is set to "2" on the cutter graduations in line with the index mark. This will cut a 2-inch hole.

end or ends where the wood might split with an auger bit (Fig. 25-15), (c) boring holes in end grain (Fig. 25-

25-12. Fastening the work before using an expansion bit. Notice that a piece of scrap stock has been placed under the work.

25-13. A Foerstner bit.

16), and (d) enlarging an existing hole. (This can't be done with an auger bit.) Foerstner bits are numbered the same as auger bits. The sizes range from ¼ inch to 2 inches.

1. Locate the center of the hole. With dividers draw a circle the same size as the hole.

2. If the hole should go all the way through the work, it's better to place a piece of scrap stock underneath and bore from only one side.

3. Clamp the work securely.

4. Carefully guide the bit over the circle to start the boring.

5. Use a bit gage if the hole must be bored to a certain depth.

USING A CIRCLE CUTTER. A *circle cutter* is used to cut large round holes in wood. It can also be used to make wooden wheels for toys.

QUESTIONS

1. Describe an auger bit.
2. Name the two kinds of braces.
3. How is the size of an auger bit shown?
4 What size hole will a No. 7 bit cut?

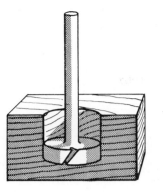

25-14. Boring a hole with a flat bottom.

25-15. Boring a hole near the end of a piece of work.

25-16. Boring a hole in end grain to make a candlestick holder.

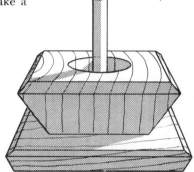

5. For what is a bit or depth gage used?
6. Tell how to install a bit in a brace.
7. Why should you have someone help you sight the tool when boring a hole?
8. How do you keep the auger bit square with the work surface?
9. What happens if you bore a hole through a piece of wood from one side and don't support it with scrap stock on the other side?
10. How can you bore to a certain depth?
11. How can you do vertical boring?
12. What is the purpose of an expansion bit?

13. Name four uses for a Foerstner bit.

Unit 26. CUTTING ON A JIG SAW

The *jig saw* has a narrow blade held in a frame. The blade cuts by jerking up and down. That's why it is called a "jig" saw. It is used to cut inside and outside curves and irregular shapes. It is a simple, safe power tool.

TOOLS

• There are many kinds and sizes of jig saws. The least expensive is a *vibrator* (moves rapidly to and fro). This type uses the same blades as the coping saw. That is, the blades have little pins at either end. It will cut only thin wood and plastic. The *rocker-action jig saw* has a motor that rocks the whole inside frame. The cutting action is smooth and even. This type reduces vibration and blade breakage. Fig. 26-1. It is an excellent machine for most work. The *belt-driven jig saw* has a belt and pulley arrangement· that controls its speed. The blade has no pins and is mounted in the upper and lower

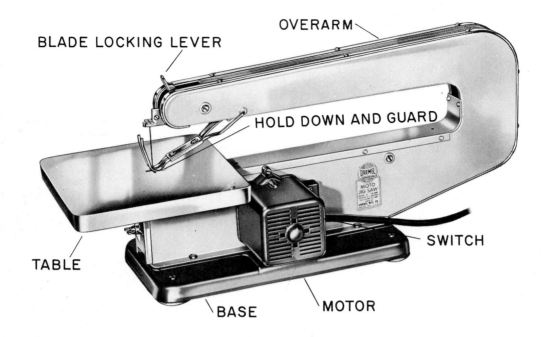

OVERARM

BLADE LOCKING LEVER

HOLD DOWN AND GUARD

SWITCH

TABLE

BASE   MOTOR

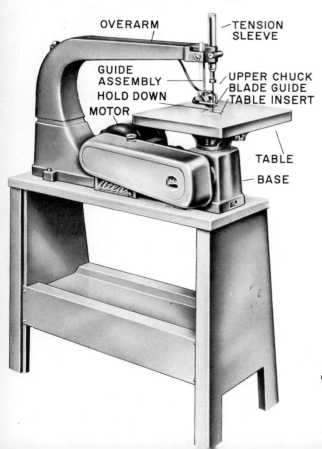

26-2. A belt-driven 18-inch jig saw.

OVERARM

TENSION SLEEVE

GUIDE ASSEMBLY
HOLD DOWN
MOTOR

UPPER CHUCK
BLADE GUIDE
TABLE INSERT

TABLE

BASE

26-1. A rocker-action jig saw. This is a 15-inch jig saw that will cut wood up to 1¾ inches thick, and 1-inch plywood. It can also be used to cut plastics, light metal and other materials.

chucks. Fig. 26-2. Jig-saw size is determined by the distance from the blade to the inside of the frame. A 15-inch jig saw, for example, will cut to the center of a 30-inch circle.

• *Power jig-saw blades* are made with either a blank end for larger machines or with pin or bent ends for smaller ones. Blades are 3, 5, or 6 inches long and have from seven to twenty teeth per inch. The thinner the work to be sawed, the more teeth the blade should have. A good rule to follow is to make sure that three teeth touch the work at all times. *Jeweler's piercing-saw blades* can be used in power jig saws to cut metal. These come in widths from very fine (6/0 is about 1/16 inch wide) to rather wide blades (about 3/16 inch).

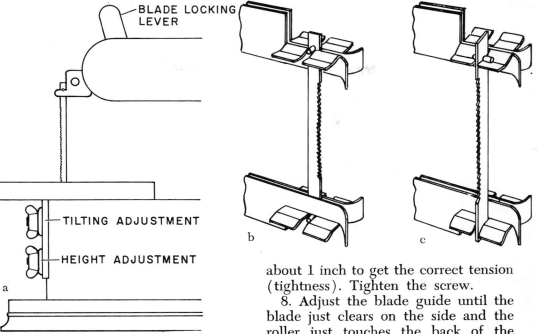

26-3. Installing a jig-saw blade in a rocker-action saw. (a) Blade-locking lever and table adjustments. (b) Blade installed for cutting from the front. (c) Blade installed for long cutting from the side.

INSTALLING A BLADE IN A BELT-DRIVEN JIG SAW

1. Remove the table insert (throat plate) in the table.

2. Loosen the knob that tilts the table and pull the right side of the table up. Turn the belt until the lower chuck is at the highest point.

3. Loosen the jaws in the lower chuck. Either a thumb screw or an Allen wrench placed in the set screw is used to do this.

4. Fasten a blade of the correct size in the lower chuck. *The teeth point down.*

5. Loosen the screw that releases the tension sleeve and lower it.

6. Fasten the other end of the blade in the upper chuck.

7. Now lift up on the tension sleeve

about 1 inch to get the correct tension (tightness). Tighten the screw.

8. Adjust the blade guide until the blade just clears on the side and the roller just touches the back of the blade.

9. Replace the throat plate. Level the table and tighten it.

10. Place the work on the table. Lower the guide until the *holddown* holds the work firmly on the table.

11. Turn the saw over by hand once to see if it runs freely.

12. Adjust the speed. For the fastest speed, place the belt on the largest motor pulley and the smallest machine pulley. Use this speed with a very fine blade and thin material. Set the machine to a slower speed for a wider blade and thicker stock.

INSTALLING A BLADE IN A ROCKER-ACTION MACHINE

1. Select a blade of the correct width and length (3 inches) with pin ends.

2. Release the blade-locking lever. Fig. 26-3.

3. Hold the blade *with the teeth pointing down.*

4. Slip the lower end into the V opening.

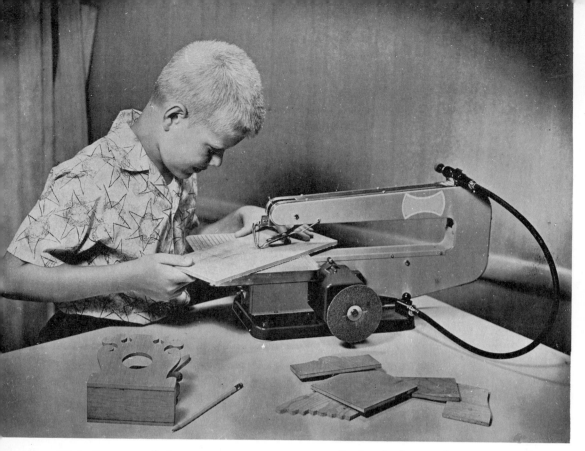

26-4. Cutting with the jig saw. It is important to cut slowly and follow the layout line carefully. Avoid "crowding" the work into the blade especially on sharp curves.

5. Pull down the upper end and slip the other end of the blade into this V opening.

6. Tighten the blade-locking lever.

7. For sawing long lengths, the blade can be put in sideways.

Cutting With a Jig Saw

1. Stand directly in front of the saw so you can guide the work with both hands.

2. Apply forward pressure with your thumbs and guide the work with your other fingers.

3. Start in the waste stock and cut up to the layout line.

4. Carefully guide the work so the saw stays just outside the line. Never force the work into the blade. Fig. 26-4.

5. At sharp corners turn the work slowly without pressing forward. If you turn the work too fast, the blade will break. Never twist the blade.

6. For inside cutting, first drill or bore a hole in the waste stock. Loosen the upper end of the blade and slip it through the hole. Fasten the upper end again in the chuck. Cut from the waste stock up to the layout line and then around the line to make the opening or design. Fig. 26-5.

26-5. Doing internal cutting on the jig saw. Drill a 3/16-inch hole into the waste area for inserting the blade.

7. For angle sawing, the table on many machines can be tilted as much as 45 degrees.

Questions

1. What can you make on a jig saw?
2. Describe three kinds of jig saws.
3. How do you choose the correct blade for a jig saw?
4. What kind of blade would you use to saw metal on the jig saw?
5. Describe the way to install a blade in a belt-driven jig saw.
6. What are the common causes of blade breakage?
7. Tell how to cut an inside opening with a jig saw.
8. Find out what an Allen wrench is. What is a set screw?

Unit 27. USING A DRILL PRESS

A *drill press* is a machine for drilling and boring holes. It can also do sanding, planing, shaping, and many other operations.

Tools

• A *bench-type drill press* is the most common. Fig. 27-1. The size is shown by the distance from the drill to the column. For example, a 15-inch drill press will bore a hole through the center of a round table top 15 inches in diameter. A key chuck holds the cutting tools.

• A *drill-press vise* holds small pieces of work. Fig. 27-2. Larger pieces can be held in the hand or clamped to the table.

27-1. Parts of a drill press.

27-2. Holding the work in a vise for drilling.

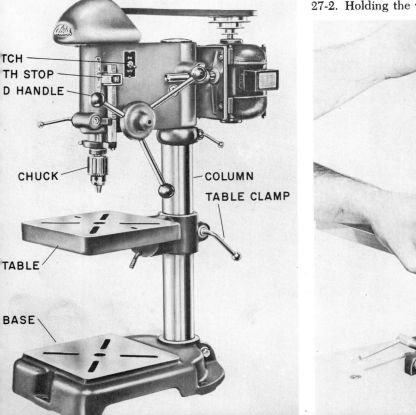

TCH
TH STOP
D HANDLE
CHUCK
COLUMN
TABLE CLAMP
TABLE
BASE

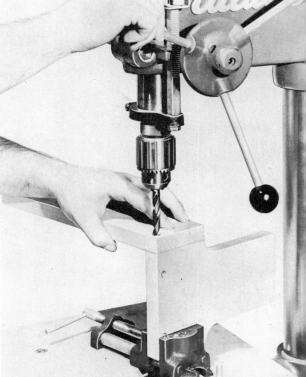

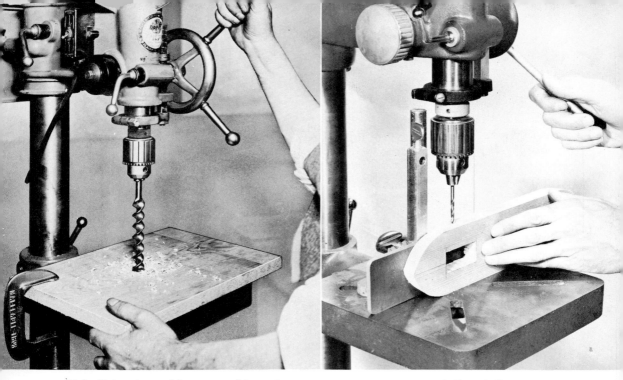

27-3. Using a machine auger bit to bore a hole. The work is clamped to the table with a C clamp.

• *Machine auger bits* have a straight *shank* and a *brad point*. Fig. 27-3. Never try to use hand auger bits in the drill press, since only a straight shank will fit into the chuck. Fig. 27-4 shows a set of *speed bits* that work well in a drill press or electric hand drill. Ma-

27-5. Using a twist drill to drill a small hole.

chine Foerstner and expansion bits are also available.
• *Twist drills* like those used in a hand drill are best for drilling small holes. Fig. 27-5. See Unit 24.

DRILLING OR BORING HOLES

1. Select the correct cutting tool and fasten it in the chuck. Rotate the drill by hand to make sure it runs straight. *Always remember to remove the chuck key.* Never try to fasten a square shank in a chuck.

2. Place the work on the table over a piece of scrap stock. Adjust the table up or down until the work just clears under the cutting tool.

3. Adjust the speed according to cutting-tool size and the kind of work. You get the fastest speed by using the *largest pulley on the motor* and *the smallest pulley on the drill.* Fast speed is for

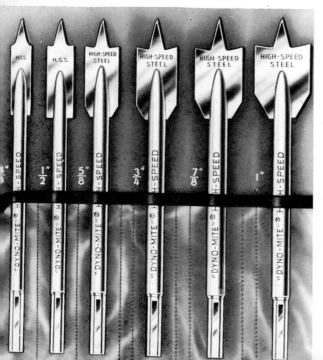

27-4. Speed-steel bits that work very well in a drill press.

94

small-diameter cutting tools and soft-woods. Speeds should be slow for large bits and hardwoods.

4. Turn on the power. Hold the work firmly with your left hand. If the piece is small or the bit large (such as an expansion bit), clamp the work in a vise or to the table with hand screws or C clamps.

5. Apply light pressure on the feed handle to cut the hole.

6. Release the pressure slightly as the tool cuts through the bottom of the work.

7. A *sanding disc* can be fastened to the chuck to sand the ends and edges of wood. Fig. 27-6.

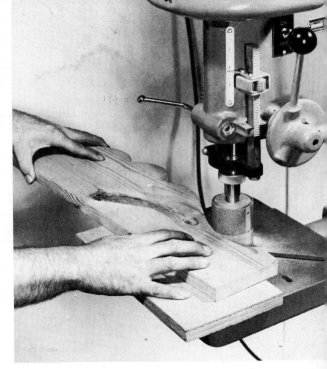

27-6. Sanding an edge on a drill press.

QUESTIONS

1. What are some of the things you can do on a drill press?

2. Name the important parts of a drill press.

3. What kind of auger bits do you need to use in a drill press?

4. How do these differ from the auger bits used in a brace?

5. What kind of cutting tool is usually used for drilling small holes?

6. How do you adjust the speed on a drill press?

7. Why should a piece of scrap wood be placed under your work on the table?

Unit 28. USING NAILS

Nails are used to hold wood pieces together. Nailing is one of the most common ways of assembling projects. Although it seems very simple, nailing takes a good deal of skill. Just watch an experienced carpenter drive nails and you'll appreciate his skill.

28-A1. Driving a nail. Remember the six basic machines, page 41. The hammer is a *lever*. As you see, it is used here as an extension of the *lever* that is your arm. By using the hammer you increase the speed and distance the force moves. This force drives the nail into the wood. Here, less force over longer distance gives greater force over shorter distance (the amount the nail moves with each blow). The nail goes in easier when it has a sharp point (wedge). Try starting a nail that has no point.

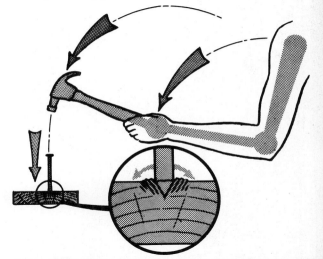

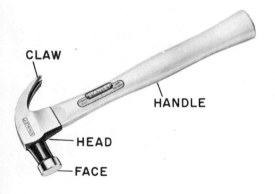

CLAW

HANDLE

HEAD

FACE

28-1. Parts of a hammer. (Stanley Tools)

TOOLS AND MATERIALS

• The *claw hammer* has either a wood or metal handle. Some workers like the metal handle. Others prefer the wood because it doesn't vibrate so much. Hammer size is shown by weight and varies from 5 to 20 ounces. A 13-ounce hammer is good for average work. Fig. 28-1.

• There are many kinds of nails. The four used the most are *common, box,*

casing, and *finishing.* Most nails are made of mild steel or aluminum. Aluminum nails have the advantage of not rusting when used out of doors. *Common nails* are for rough construction such as home building. *Box nails* are somewhat smaller and are used where the common nails might split out the wood, such as in building boxes or crates. *Casing nails* have a smaller head and are used in interior trim in houses and in cabinet making. *Finishing nails* have small heads and are ideal for project making, cabinet work, and finished carpentry.

Nail size is given by the term "penny," which is shown by the letter "d". No one knows exactly where this term comes from. Some people think it meant the cost of nails in pence (English money), while others thought it meant the weight per thousand. In either case, the term is still used. For example, a 3d nail is 1¼ inches long; a 6d nail is 2 inches long. While a 6d common and a 6d finishing nail are both 2 inches long, the common nail is

NAIL CHART

Size	Length in Inches	American Steel Wire Gage Number		
		Common	Box and Casing	Finishing
2d	1	15*	15½	16½
3d	1¼	14	14½	15½
4d	1½	12½	14	15
5d	1¾	12½	14	15
6d	2	11½	12½	13
7d	2¼	11½	12½	13
8d	2½	10¼	11½	12½
9d	2¾	10¼	11½	12½
10d	3	9	10½	11½
12d	3¼	9	10½	11½
16d	3½	8	10	11
20d	4	6	9	10
30d	4½	5	9	
40d	5	4	8	

*Note: The decimal equivalent of common gage numbers is:

15 = .072	12 = .106	9 = .148	6 = .192
14 = .080	11 = .121	8 = .162	5 = .207
13 = .092	10 = .135	7 = .177	4 = .225

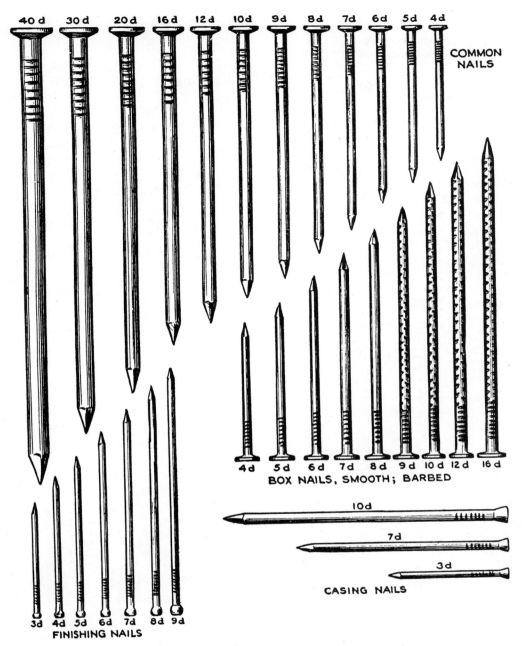

40 d 30 d 20 d 16 d 12 d 10 d 9 d 8 d 7 d 6 d 5 d 4 d

COMMON NAILS

4 d 5 d 6 d 7 d 8 d 9 d 10 d 12 d 16 d

BOX NAILS, SMOOTH; BARBED

10 d

7 d

3 d

CASING NAILS

3 d 4 d 5 d 6 d 7 d 8 d 9 d

FINISHING NAILS

28-2. Kinds and sizes of common nails.

larger in diameter. That is because they are made from different gage wire (shown by a number)—11½ gage for common, 13 gage for finishing.

Two other small nails used in making novelties and small articles are *escutch-eon pins* and *wire brads*. Escutcheon pins are small brass nails with round heads. They come in lengths from ¼ inch to 1¼ inches and in diameters from 20 gage to 16 gage. Wire brads are small, flat-headed, mild-steel nails with sharp points. They come in

28-3. Nail set. (Stanley Tools)

lengths from ½ inch to 1½ inches, in gage numbers from 20 to 14. Notice that you can get these fasteners at a given length in several gages (diameters). Fig. 28-2.

• A *nail set* is a small metal punch with a cupped end. The cupped end prevents it from slipping off the head of the nail. The tool is used to sink the heads of casing or finishing nails below the wood surface. Fig. 28-3.

DRIVING NAILS

1. Decide on the size and kind of nails you need. Choose the smallest diameter that will do the job. A nail too large will split the wood. Nails should be a little shorter than the thick-- ness of the pieces being nailed. In some cases nails are driven through and stick out the other side. Then the nail is *clinched* (bent over) with the grain.

2. Decide on the number and location of the nails. The nails should be evenly spaced but *staggered* (not in a straight line). Don't put several nails along the same grain line, as this will split the wood. When nailing hardwood, put a little wax or soap on the point of the nail so it goes in easier. If you think there is danger of splitting the wood, first drill a hole that is smaller than the nail (about three fourths the diameter of the nail).

3. Hold the nail between your thumb and forefinger. Grasp the hammer handle near its end. Tap the nail lightly to start it. Take your hand away from the nail. Fig. 28-4.

4. Drive the nail by swinging the hammer and your arm as a unit. Use

28-4. Holding the nail and hammer in preparation for nailing.

28-5. Hit the nail squarely with a few good, solid blows.

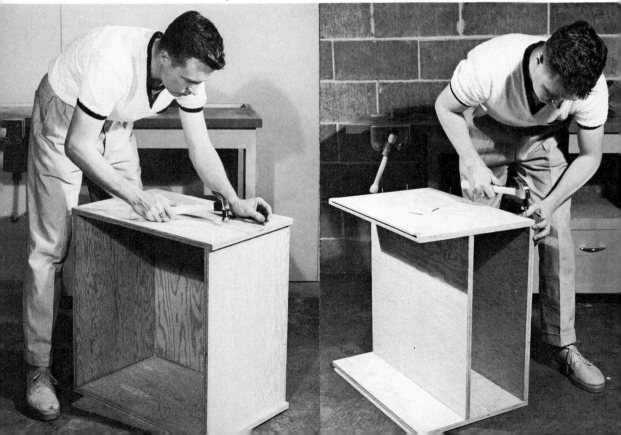

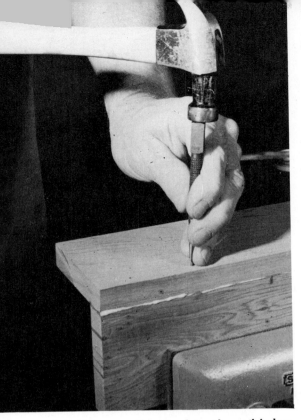

28-6. Using a nail set to drive the nail below the surface of the wood.

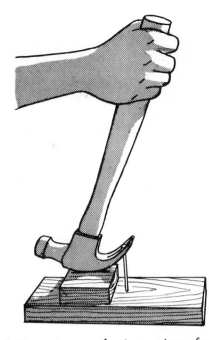

28-7. Removing a nail using a piece of scrap wood under the head of the hammer. This increases the leverage of the hammer.

just a little wrist movement. Strike the nail with a few good blows, keeping your eye on the nail. Fig. 28-5.

5. If the nail bends, don't try to straighten it by striking it on the side. Remove the nail and use a new one. Nails driven at an angle have better holding power. When nailing into end grain, drive the first nail in straight and the other nails at an angle.

6. If the nail is a casing or finishing nail, drive it until the head still shows. Then use a nail set with a point slightly smaller than the head of the nail. Place the point of the nail set over the head of the nail, guiding it with your fourth finger as shown in Fig. 28-6. Drive the head a little below the surface (about 1/16 inch).

REMOVING NAILS

1. To remove nails from a board or

to pull out a bent nail, use the claw of the hammer head. Slip the claw under the nail head and pull the handle down.

2. On finished surfaces, place a thin board or piece of plywood under the claw to protect the surface. If the nail is quite long, put a thick block under the claw after the nail is part way out. This helps to keep the nail straight and gives you better leverage. Fig. 28-7.

28-8. The correct method of toenailing.

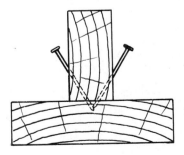

28-9. Using a corrugated fastener to reinforce a miter joint. This fastener has greater strength than an ordinary nail. It should always be installed diagonally.

TOENAILING. This is a way of fastening the end of one board to the edge or face of another. The nails are driven at an angle from either side of the first board. This helps to hold the boards tightly together. Fig. 28-8.

USING CORRUGATED FASTENERS. These are a kind of wiggle nail used in general construction and repair work. They are often used, for example, in holding the corners of window screens together. Place them at an angle to the grain. Never place them straight with the grain, as this could split the wood. Fig. 28-9.

QUESTIONS

1. Name the parts of a claw hammer.
2. What is a nail set and how is it used?
3. Name four common kinds of nails.
4. What is the difference between a casing nail and a finishing nail?
5. What does the term "penny" mean?
6. Describe an escutcheon pin.
7. Why should nails be staggered?
8. What is the difference between a brad and a finishing nail?
9. Describe the way to start nailing.
10. What can you put on a nail to make it easier to drive into hardwood?
11. How do you remove a nail?
12. What is toenailing?
13. Describe the way to use corrugated fasteners.

Unit 29. INSTALLING SCREWS

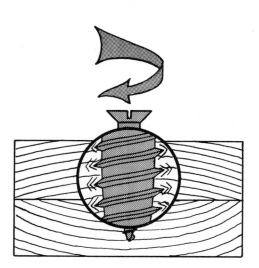

A *screw* is a fastener with a groove twisting around part of its length. It is one of the best wood fasteners. A screw is strong. It does not come out easily. It can be tightened and loosened again later to take an article apart.

29-A1. A wood screw is the most efficient device for holding pieces together. A force applied to the head causes the screw to overcome resistance and move into the wood. Thus it moves a long distance, yet one complete turn of the screw moves it straight into the wood only a distance from the top of one thread to the top of the next. See discussion of simple machines, page 41. The thread itself is an *inclined plane*.

100

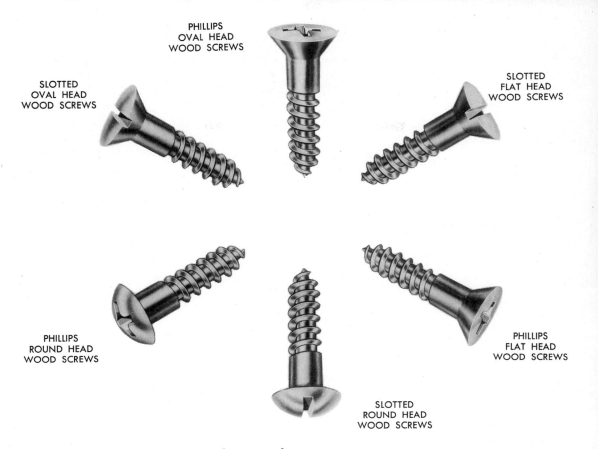

PHILLIPS
OVAL HEAD
WOOD SCREWS

SLOTTED
OVAL HEAD
WOOD SCREWS

SLOTTED
FLAT HEAD
WOOD SCREWS

PHILLIPS
ROUND HEAD
WOOD SCREWS

PHILLIPS
FLAT HEAD
WOOD SCREWS

SLOTTED
ROUND HEAD
WOOD SCREWS

29-1. Common head shapes and types of slots.

TOOLS AND MATERIALS

• *Wood screws* are made of mild steel, brass, aluminum, and copper. Brass screws are used for boats, water skis, or other projects used around water. The most common head shapes are *round, flat,* and *oval.* Fig. 29-1. Round-head screws of mild steel are made with a blue finish. Flat-head screws of mild steel have a bright finish. Oval-head screws are usually plated with cadmium or chromium and are used most often to install hinges, hooks, and other hardware. Most screws have a plain *slotted head.* However, the *recessed* (Phillips) head is becoming more popular. Screws come in different lengths from ¼ inch to 6 inches. They also come in different gage sizes from O,

the smallest, to 24, the largest. The gage tells the diameter. The larger the number, the greater the diameter. Screws of the same length come in different gage sizes. For example, a No. 6 screw, 1½ inches long, is a very slim screw, while a No. 14 screw, 1½ inches long, is a fat screw. Fig. 29-3. Generally the lower gage numbers are used for thin wood and the larger numbers for heavy wood. Screws are sold by the dozen in hardware stores. They are packed in factories by the box. A box contains one gross. Fig. 29-2.

29-2. The boxtop shows how screws are marked. The box contains one gross of No. 5 flat-head steel screws that are ⅝ inch long.

SOUTHERN SCREW CO.
WOOD SCREWS
FLAT
HEAD
STEEL
1 GROSS
MADE IN U.S.A.
⅝   5

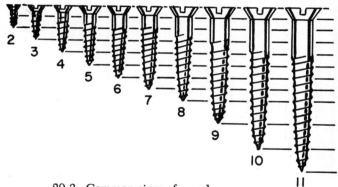

CHARTED BELOW ARE SCREW LENGTHS FROM ¼″ TO 4″ WITH SHANK DIMENSIONS FROM 0 TO 20. THESE SIZES ARE GENERALLY AVAILABLE AND ARE THE ONES MOST FREQUENTLY USED.

29-3. Common sizes of wood screws.

LENGTH	SHANK NUMBERS																
	0	1	2	3	4	5	6	7	8	9	10	11	12	14	16	18	20
¼ inch	0	1	2	3													
⅜ inch			2	3	4	5	6	7									
½ inch			2	3	4	5	6	7	8								
⅝ inch				3	4	5	6	7	8	9	10						
¾ inch					4	5	6	7	8	9	10	11					
⅞ inch							6	7	8	9	10	11	12				
1 inch							6	7	8	9	10	11	12	14			
1¼ inch								7	8	9	10	11	12	14	16		
1½ inch							6	7	8	9	10	11	12	14	16	18	
1¾ inch									8	9	10	11	12	14	16	18	20
2 inch									8	9	10	11	12	14	16	18	20
2¼ inch										9	10	11	12	14	16	18	20
2½ inch													12	14	16	18	20
2¾ inch														14	16	18	20
3 inch															16	18	20
3½ inch																18	20
4 inch																18	20
0 TO 24 DIAMETER DIMENSIONS IN INCHES AT BODY	.060	.073	.086	.099	.112	.125	.138	.151	.164	.177	.190	.203	.216	.242	.268	.294	.320

The five most common sizes of flat-head screws are: No. 7—¾ inch long, No. 8—1 inch long, No. 8—1¼ inch long, No. 10—1¼ inch long, and No. 12—1½ inch long.

• There are two types of screw drivers. The *plain screw driver* is used to in-

29-4. Parts of a screw driver. (Stanley Tools)

TIP   BLADE   HANDLE

29-5. Recessed, or Phillips, head screw driver. (Stanley Tools)

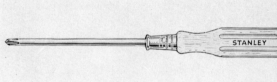

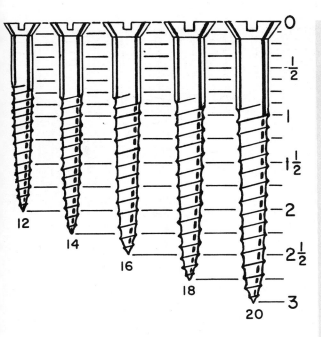

29-6. (a) Countersink for brace. (b) Countersink for hand drill or drill press. (Stanley Tools)

29-7. Screw-driver bit. (Stanley Tools)

stall slotted-head screws. The size depends on the length and diameter of the blade. Fig. 29-4. The *Phillips-head screw driver* is also made in different diameters and lengths. Fig. 29-5. It cannot be reshaped.

• An *82-degree countersink* is needed for flat-head screws that must be flush with the surface. It makes a cone-shaped hole for the head of the screw to go into. Fig. 29-6 (a) shows a type used in a brace. Fig. 29-6 (b) shows a kind to use in a hand drill or drill press.

• A *screw-driver bit* can be used in a brace for setting screws. Fig. 29-7.

29-8. Drill sizes for screws.

Screw Gage No.	0	1	2	3	4	5	6	7	8	9	10	11	12	14	16	18	20
Shank Hole Hard & Soft wood	$\frac{1}{16}$	$\frac{5}{64}$	$\frac{3}{32}$	$\frac{7}{64}$	$\frac{7}{64}$	$\frac{1}{8}$	$\frac{9}{64}$	$\frac{5}{32}$	$\frac{11}{64}$	$\frac{3}{16}$	$\frac{3}{16}$	$\frac{13}{64}$	$\frac{7}{32}$	$\frac{1}{4}$	$\frac{17}{64}$	$\frac{19}{64}$	$\frac{21}{64}$
PILOT HOLE SOFT WOOD	$\frac{1}{64}$	$\frac{1}{32}$	$\frac{1}{32}$	$\frac{3}{64}$	$\frac{3}{64}$	$\frac{1}{16}$	$\frac{1}{16}$	$\frac{1}{16}$	$\frac{5}{64}$	$\frac{5}{64}$	$\frac{3}{32}$	$\frac{3}{32}$	$\frac{7}{64}$	$\frac{7}{64}$	$\frac{9}{64}$	$\frac{9}{64}$	$\frac{11}{64}$
PILOT HOLE HARD WOOD	$\frac{1}{32}$	$\frac{1}{32}$	$\frac{3}{64}$	$\frac{1}{16}$	$\frac{1}{16}$	$\frac{5}{64}$	$\frac{5}{64}$	$\frac{3}{32}$	$\frac{3}{32}$	$\frac{7}{64}$	$\frac{7}{64}$	$\frac{1}{8}$	$\frac{1}{8}$	$\frac{9}{64}$	$\frac{5}{32}$	$\frac{3}{16}$	$\frac{13}{64}$
Auger Bit Sizes For Plug Hole			3	4	4	4	5	5	6	6	6	7	7	8	9	10	11

29-9. Center punching in preparation for drilling the pilot, or anchor, hole.

INSTALLING SCREWS

1. Choose a screw long enough to go two thirds its length into the second part. Another rule to follow is to make sure that all the threaded part of the screw will go into the second part. The diameter of the screw should be chosen according to the thickness of the wood.

2. Mark the location of the screw hole. Make a punch mark with a center punch or scratch awl.

3. Select a drill that will be equal in diameter to the *shank* of the screw and drill a *shank hole* in the first part. A chart shows correct drill size. Fig. 29-8. You can also hold the drill behind the screw shank and sight for size.

4. Place the first piece of wood over the second and punch a hole with a scratch awl or nail. Fig. 29-9.

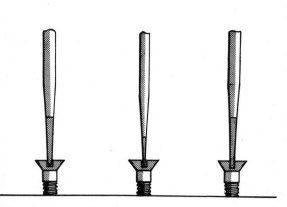

29-11. Incorrect and correct way of grinding a screw driver for slotted-head screws: (a) Tip rounded. (b) Tip too thin. (c) Tip properly fitted.

5. Drill a *pilot, or anchor, hole* to the depth the screw will go. If the wood is very soft, this hole may not be needed. The drill for the pilot hole must be about equal to the smallest diameter of the threaded part of the screw. Here again you can use a chart or sight for size. Use a depth or bit gage if several screws must be installed.

6. When using flat-head screws, cut a conical (cone-shaped) hole with a countersink so the head of the screw will be flush with the surface. Fig. 29-10. To check, turn the screw upside down and see if the hole is just right. If you are installing many screws of the same size, put a depth or bit gage on the countersink.

7. The blade of the screw driver should be equal to the width of the screw head. Fig. 29-11. A screw driver that is too small will slip and make a *burr* (a rough edge) on the screw head. A screw driver that is too large will mar the wood as you finish tightening the screw. Fig. 29-12. The tool should

29-10. Steps in installing a flat-head screw: (a) Drill the *shank hole.* (b) Drill the *pilot, or anchor, hole.* (c) Countersink. (d) Check the amount of countersink with the screw head. (e) Install the flat-head screw. (f) Screw properly installed.

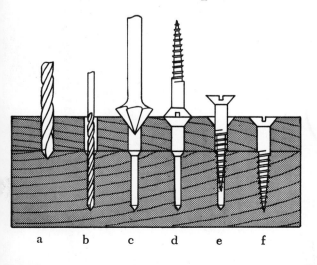

a   b   c   d   e   f

104

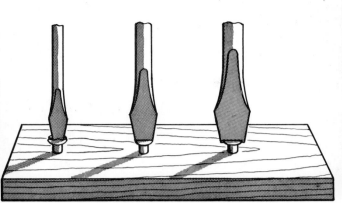

29-12. Correct and incorrect sizes of screw drivers: (a) Too small—has ruined the slot in the head. (b) Correct size. (c) Too large—will scratch the wood.

29-14. Use steady, even pressure to install a screw with a screw-driver bit. Be careful not to allow the bit to slip.

be properly ground to have a straight, square blade.

8. Hold the screw between your thumb and forefinger and the handle of the screwdriver lightly in your right hand. Start the screw. Then slip your left hand up back of the tip of the screwdriver to guide the tool as you tighten the screw. Fig. 29-13.

9. Don't try to tighten the screw too much. You may break the screw or strip the threads in the wood, and the fastener won't hold. You must be especially careful with aluminum or brass screws.

10. If several screws are used to

29-13. Starting a screw. Note that the screw is held between the thumb and forefinger to start it correctly.

fasten two parts together, it is a good idea first to drill all the shank holes (and countersink). Then drill one pilot hole and install the screw before drilling the other pilot holes. You will find it is easier to line up the parts to be put together.

11. In driving a large number of screws, a *screw-driver bit* may be used in a brace to speed the work. Fig. 29-14.

USING A SCREW MATE. A *screw-mate drill countersink* is a good tool to use with flat-head screws. It will do four things:

29-15. A screw-mate drill and countersink to use with flat-head screws. (Stanley Tools)

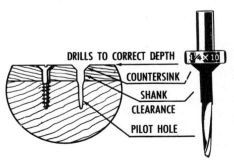

DRILLS TO CORRECT DEPTH

COUNTERSINK

SHANK
CLEARANCE

PILOT HOLE

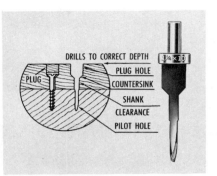

29-16. A screw-mate counterbore which does five things at once. A wood plug can be used to cover the screw head. (Stanley Tools)

1. Drill to the correct depth.
2. Do countersinking.
3. Make the correct shank clearance.
4. Make the correct pilot hole.

The tool is stamped with the gage number and length. For example, one marked 1¼ inches by 10 gage would be used for a flathead screw 1¼ inches long in a No. 10 gage size. Fig. 29-15.

A *counterbore* will do all the operations performed by the screw mate, plus drilling plug holes for wooden plugs. Fig. 29-16.

CONCEALING THE SCREW HEAD. On some projects you don't want the screw head to show. As a first step, bore a shallow hole with an auger bit that is the same diameter as the screw head. Then, after the screw is set, you can cover the screw with plastic wood or a plug. Fig. 29-17. A plain plug or button (small wood covering) can be cut on the drill press, or a decorative plug can be purchased from a supply house.

HOUSEHOLD SCREW DEVICES. Fig. 29-18 shows some of the common household screw devices. Common sizes of *cup hooks* (usually made of brass) are ½, ⅝, ¾, 1, 1¼ and 1½ inch. *Screw hooks* are made in lengths from 1¼ to 2½ inches. "L" (square-

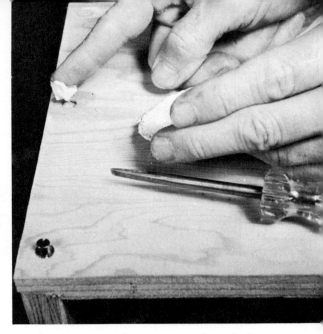

29-17. Screws can be countersunk and the hole filled with wood dough or water putty. Remember when adding a filler to apply it so it is slightly higher than the wood. Then sand it off level after it is dry.

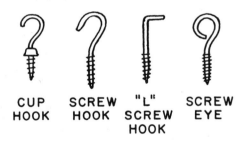

| CUP HOOK | SCREW HOOK | "L" SCREW HOOK | SCREW EYE |

29-18. Special household screw devices.

bent) *screw hooks* are available in lengths from 1 inch to 2¼ inches. *Screw eyes* are made with either small or medium eyes in many different sizes.

QUESTIONS

1. Why is a screw better than a nail?
2. Name some of the materials from which screws are made.
3. What are the most common head shapes?
4. Which is larger in diameter, a No. 4 or a No. 10 screw?
5. Name the most common sizes of flathead screws.

6. When is an 82-degree countersink needed?

7. How do you choose the correct size screw?

8. What is a shank hole?

9. What is a pilot, or anchor, hole?

10. Tell how to install a screw.

11. Why is a screw mate a convenient tool to have?

12. How can you hide the heads of screws?

13. Describe common household screw devices.

Unit 30. COMMON JOINTS AND THEIR USES

Furniture, houses, and the articles you make in the shop are all assembled with *joints*. While there are over 100 different kinds of joints, most of them are somewhat alike. Only eight are really

30-1. Common woodworking joints.

COMMON WOOD JOINTS

Kinds	Uses	How Made	Similar Kinds
EDGE	For tops of tables, chairs, desks and other furniture needing large surfaces.	Plane a square edge on both pieces. Add dowel or spline for strength. Glue.	Dowel, Tongue and Groove, and Rabbet.
BUTT	For simple boxes, cases, cheap drawers, frames and chairs.	Cut corners square in a miter box. Fasten with nails or screws and/or glue. Use doweling jig for corner dowel joint.	Glued and blocked and doweled corner for greater strength.
RABBET	For corners of modern furniture, simple drawer construction and boxes.	Cut rabbet with back saw. Glue, nail or fasten with long screws.	Dado and rabbet for good drawer corners.
DADO	For shelves, steps, drawers and book cases.	Cut with back saw and trim out with router plane or chisel. Fit second piece into dado. Glue.	Blind dado (gain) for front edge that doesn't show joint.
MITER	For frames of pictures, boxes, molding around doors or furniture.	Cut with miter box. Fit corners carefully. Fasten with glue, nails or corrugated fasteners.	Dowel or spline for greater strength.
LAP	For legs of furniture, doors, frames and braces.	Make like two dadoes. Assemble with glue.	End lap for frames. Middle lap for doors.
MORTISE AND TENON	For best chair, table and chest construction.	Cut tenon with back saw. Drill out mortise on drill press. Trim out with chisel.	Open mortise and tenon for frames. Haunched mortise and tenon for panel construction.
DOVETAIL	For best drawer and box construction. Furniture corners.	Cut dovetail with jig saw. Glue.	Secret dovetail for quality furniture.

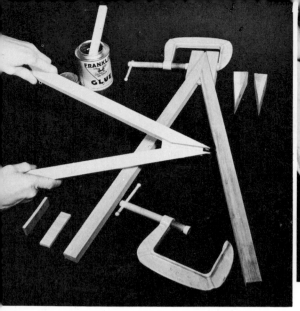

30-3. A simple edge joint.

30-2. (a) A *spline* is a good device for joining two pieces of wood without nails. A groove or slot is cut in each piece and then a thin piece of wood is inserted and glued in place. This strengthens the joint. (b) A good example of the use of a spline in making stacking tables.

different from each other. You will use the simpler ones when you build the projects shown in this book. The more difficult joints are found in fine furniture, and are usually made with machines. When you take an advanced

30-4. At the left is a simple butt joint. At the right is a butt joint that has been glued and blocked. Adding this triangular piece to the wood strengthens the joint.

30-5. Rabbet joints are often used in making boxes and drawers. This joint can be made with or across the grain.

course in woodworking, you will have a chance to make some of these. Fig. 30-1.

MAKING JOINTS STRONGER. Joints are held together with glue or with glue plus nails or screws. Sometimes a joint is made stronger by adding a *dowel* or *spline*. See Unit 31. A spline is a thin piece of wood inserted in a groove between the two parts of a joint. Fig. 30-2.

EDGE JOINT. In an edge joint boards are fastened together to make a larger piece. Fig. 30-3. For instance, the top of a table can be made in this way. The simplest is a plain edge joint in which the edges are planed and then glued together. Often dowels or a spline are added for strength. A *rabbet* (slot) cut on both pieces also strengthens the joint. The *tongue-and-groove joint* has a groove cut along one edge and a tongue along the other. The floor boards in many homes are put together with tongue-and-groove joints.

BUTT JOINT. A butt joint is very simple. The end of one piece is fastened to the surface or edge of the other. Fig. 30-4. It is used to make a simple

box or to fasten two pieces at right angles. The butt joint is a popular one for house building. Dowels or a corner block are sometimes added to make the joint stronger.

RABBET JOINT. In a *rabbet joint* the first piece fits into a groove cut across the end or edge of the second piece. Fig. 30-5. It is found in simple furniture and in some box construction.

30-6. The dado joint is shown at the right. The dado-and-rabbet joint at the left is used on better drawer construction.

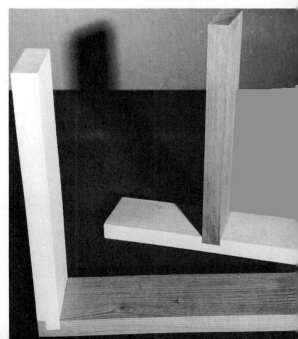

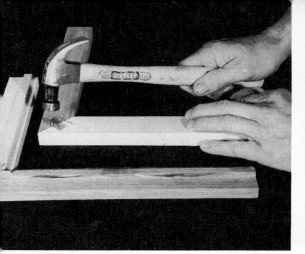

30-7. The miter joint is used to make frames, moldings, and corners on modern furniture. This window-screen frame is being fastened with corrugated fasteners.

30-9. The mortise-and-tenon joint is found in the best type furniture. The blind mortise-and-tenon joint (at the left) is used to fasten rails to legs on tables, chairs, and similar furniture. The one on the right is called an open mortise-and-tenon joint.

DADO JOINT. A *dado joint* is a good one for shelves, steps, bookcases, book racks, chests and other types of cabinets. Fig. 30-6. A blind *dado,* or *gain,* is one in which the dado is cut only part way across the board. A notch must be cut out of the second piece. This makes it look better from the front edge because the dado doesn't show. The *dado and rabbet* is a good joint for drawers.

MITER JOINT. In a *miter joint* the corners are cut at an angle, usually 45 degrees, forming a right angle. A picture frame is a good example. Trim around doors and windows is made with a miter joint. A way to strengthen

this joint is to use a dowel, spline, or key (a thin piece of wood inserted across the corner) Fig. 30-7.

LAP JOINT. The *cross-lap joint* is made when two pieces of wood must cross. You find it on frames, table legs, and some kinds of chairs (especially summer furniture). Fig. 30-8. The carpenter often uses it to strengthen the frame of a house. The pieces may cross at any angle. Other common kinds are the *middle lap* and the *end lap.* Lap joints are made in the same way as rabbet or dado joints.

MORTISE-AND-TENON JOINT. The *mortise-and-tenon joint* is one of the strong-

30-8. The cross-lap joint is used in making modern furniture. Outdoor furniture frequently has this kind of joint.

30-10. The dovetail joint is found in fine box and drawer construction. The most difficult joint to make, it is found only in highest quality furniture.

est. It is found on better-quality chairs, tables, and benches. Fig. 30-9. The *mortise* is the rectangular opening and the *tenon* is the part that fits into the opening. Mortise-and-tenon joints take a lot of time and experience when made by hand. With power tools they can be made quickly.

DOVETAIL JOINT. The *dovetail joint* is used on the corners of the best drawers and boxes. Fig. 30-10. Look at a drawer on a well made chest or cabinet. The front and sides almost always have dovetail joints. This joint is very difficult to make by hand. Years ago, craftsmen did so, but we use power tools.

1. How many basic kinds of joints are there?
2. How can joints be strengthened?
3. Sketch an edge joint and tell what it is used for.
4. What is a butt joint?
5. What shape is a rabbet?
6. Name the principal uses for the dado joint.
7. At what angle is the corner of a miter joint usually cut?
8. Where are lap joints used?
9. What kind of joint is found in better-quality chairs and tables?
10. What is a mortise?
11. What is a tenon?
12. Where are dovetail joints usually found in furniture?

Unit 31. USING DOWELS

A *dowel* is a peg or pin of wood that fits into two matching holes to strengthen a joint. Dowels are also used as decoration or as parts of many small projects. Pegs on a hat rack are an example.

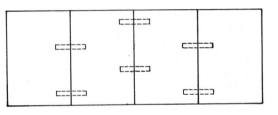

31-1. (a) The corner of this frame will be strengthened with dowels. The location of the dowels is marked first on one piece. Then the *dowel centers* are fastened in place. When the two pieces are held together, the dowel centers show the location of the holes in the second piece. (b) Some common uses of dowels.

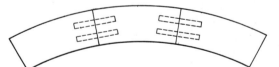

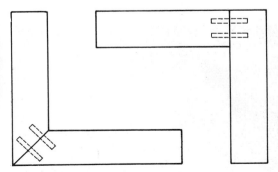

111

Tools and Materials

• *Dowel rod* is usually made of birch in 36-inch lengths. Fig. 31-1. The common diameters are 1/8 to 1 inch, measured in 1/16ths. Sometimes a groove is cut along the dowel so that glue holds better. Small *dowel pins* are made with a *spiral* groove and pointed ends. The spiral helps the piece go in easier and the glue to flow.

• A *dowel sharpener* points the ends of dowels. Fig. 31-2.

• A *doweling jig* will help locate the position of the holes and guide the auger bit for boring. This jig comes with several metal guides in sizes of 3/16, 1/4, 5/16, 3/8, 7/16, and 1/2 inch. Fig. 31-3.

• *Dowel centers* are small metal pins used for spotting the location of holes on two parts of a joint.

• *Dowel bits* are auger bits for boring

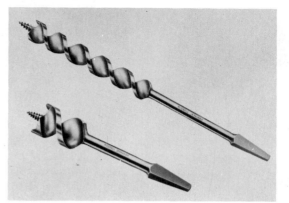

31-4. Bits for doweling. These bits are shorter than the standard auger bit. (Stanley Tools)

holes for dowels. These bits are shorter than regular auger bits. Fig. 31-4.

• Marking gage, try square, rule, and pencil.

Making a Dowel Edge Joint

1. Square up the pieces that will form the larger surface.

2. Place the pieces on the bench side by side. Arrange them with the grain running in the same direction and the *annular rings* turned in opposite directions. Fig. 31-5. This will help to prevent warping.

3. Mark the face surface with matching numbers at each joint: 1-1, 2-2, etc.

4. Check the edges to be jointed. They should be:

    a. Square with the face surface. Fig. 31-6.

    b. Straight along the length. Use a large framing or carpenter's square to test.

    c. Planed with a slight opening in the center and the ends fitting tightly.

5. Clamp the first two pieces in a vise with the face surfaces out.

6. Mark lines for the position of dowels across the edges. There should be dowels every 12 to 18 inches. If

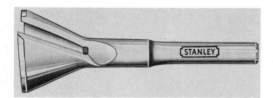

31-2. Dowel sharpener. (Stanley Tools)

31-3. Doweling jig. (Stanley Tools)

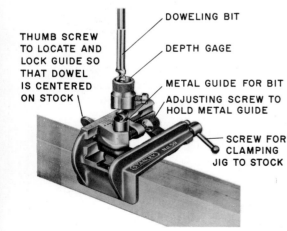

THUMB SCREW TO LOCATE AND LOCK GUIDE SO THAT DOWEL IS CENTERED ON STOCK

DOWELING BIT

DEPTH GAGE

METAL GUIDE FOR BIT

ADJUSTING SCREW TO HOLD METAL GUIDE

SCREW FOR CLAMPING JIG TO STOCK

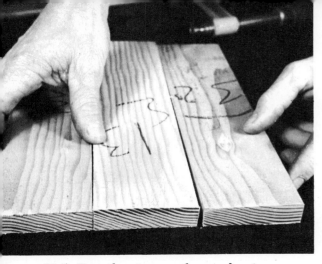

31-5. Turn the pieces so the annular rings on the ends are faced in opposite directions.

31-7. Mark the location of the dowel holes with a marking gage.

three dowels are used, place one in the center and the others about 2 or 3 inches in from either end. These are the only layout lines needed if a doweling jig is used.

7. If a doweling jig isn't used, mark centers for the holes. Use a marking gage set at half the thickness of the stock and mark from the face surfaces. Fig. 31-7.

8. Choose dowel rod equal in· diameter to about half the thickness of the stock.

9. If a doweling jig is used, proceed as follows:

• After you choose the dowel rod, select a metal guide of the same size for the doweling jig. Suppose the rod is ¼ inch. Select a guide this size and slip it into the clamp of the jig. Adjust the guide so it is centered on the thickness of stock.

• Clamp the jig over the stock so it is lined up with the cross line.

• Place the jig with the solid side against the face surface. Clamp a stop to the bit for the correct depth of hole.

10. Choose an auger bit equal to the size of the dowel. Attach a *bit gage* so the depth of holes will be about 1½ to 2 inches.

11. Use a square to line up the bit. Bore the holes to the correct depth. Make sure the holes are bored squarely

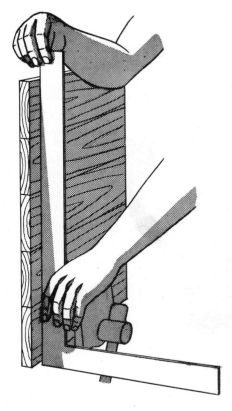

31-6. Make sure the edges are square before marking the location for the dowels. Hold a straightedge against the face surfaces.

113

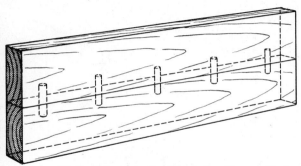

31-8. Edge joint with the dowels installed.

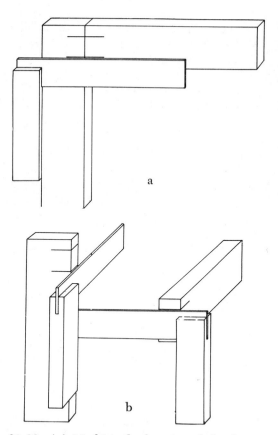

a

b

31-10. (a) Marking the location of the dowels. (b) Continuing the lines across the edge end of the pieces.

and on center. If they aren't, the two parts of the joint won't fit together right.

12.   Bore all the holes on both parts of the joint. Countersink the holes so the dowels will start easily.

13.   Cut the dowels about ⅛ to ¼ inch shorter than the combined depth of the two holes. Chamfer or point the ends.

14.   Insert the dowels in one edge and then assemble the joint to check if it fits. Fig. 31-8.

15.   Take it apart. Remove the dowels. Dip the dowels one-third way into glue and drive them into one edge with a mallet.

16.   Apply glue to this edge and to the exposed dowels.

17.   Clamp the parts as described in Unit 35.

MAKING A RAIL-TO-LEG BUTT DOWEL JOINT. This joint is used in place of a mortise-and-tenon joint on tables and chairs.

1.   Locate the position of the dowels on the leg and in the ends of the rails. Fig. 31-9. The rail may be flush with the outside of the leg or set back some distance. Remember, the dowels are

31-9. Notice that the rails are thinner than the legs. The dowels are centered on the ends of the rails and on the legs. If the rails must be flush with the surface of the legs, then the dowel holes on the legs must be closer to the outside surfaces.

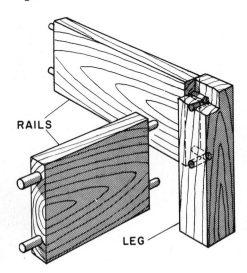

RAILS

LEG

centered in the ends of the rails. Fig. 31-10. The position of the dowel holes in the leg depends on how far back the rail will be from the edge of the leg.

2. After the holes are located, the joint is made the same way as described above.

MAKING A FRAME WITH DOWELS

1. Cut all pieces to the same thickness and width. If the frame is square, all pieces are the same length. If not, the two pairs of matching pieces must be equal.

2. Locate the position of the dowels in the ends of the two pieces and the edges of the other two pieces.

3. Complete the joint as described above. Fig. 31-11.

31-11. Gluing a dowel joint. This joint can be used in making screens or other large frames.

QUESTIONS

1. What is a dowel?
2. Of what is a dowel usually made?
3. What is the difference between dowel bits and auger bits?
4. What diameter dowel would you use on ¾-inch stock?
5. How long should the dowels be?
6. Tell how to make a dowel edge joint.
7. Tell how to make a rail-to-leg butt joint with dowels.

Unit 32. MAKING A RABBET JOINT

A *rabbet* is a slot that is cut at the end or edge of a board. Fig. 32-1. The end or edge of another piece is made to fit into this slot to make a rabbet joint. This joint is one of the simplest ones. It is used in making a box or to put together parts of furniture such as a modern table or case.

TOOLS AND MATERIALS. Marking gage, try square, back saw, pencil or knife, vise, hammer, nail set, screw driver, nails or screws, and glue.

Follow these four steps in all *jointery* (joint making):

LAYOUT.

1. Square up stock to the correct dimensions: thickness, width, and length.

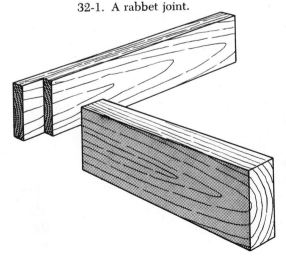

32-1. A rabbet joint.

32-2. Lay out the width of the rabbet by holding one piece over the other. Mark the width with a pencil. Also see 33-5.

2. Mark the shape of the rabbet on the end or edge of one piece.
• Measure from the end or edge a distance equal to the thickness of stock. This is the shoulder line. Mark a line across the stock with a try square and a pencil or knife.
• Another method is to place one piece of stock over the other as shown in Fig.

32-3. Making the shoulder cut. Notice that a guide board is clamped next to the layout line. Carefully cut the shoulder with a back saw. The saw kerf must be in the waste stock.

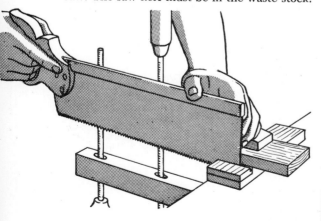

32-4. Trimming the rabbet after it has been cut.

32-2 and mark a line across. Square the lines across both edges of the first piece.

32-5. Assembling a rabbet joint with glue and nails.

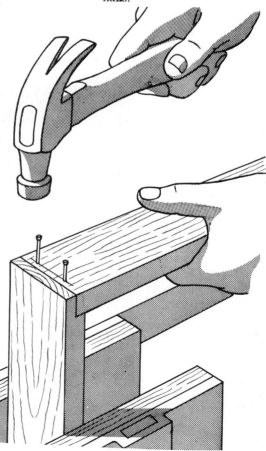

116

3. Cut the rabbet to a depth of ½ to ⅔ the thickness of the stock.

4. Adjust a marking gage to the correct depth. Mark a line across the edges and end to outline the rabbet.

CUTTING

1. Fasten the marked piece in a vise or clamp it to the top of the bench.

2. Make the shoulder cut to correct depth with a back saw. It might be a good idea to use a *guide board* for this. Fig. 32-3.

3. Clamp the work vertically in a vise and make the second cut to form the rabbet.

FITTING

1. Place the end of the second piece in the rabbet and see if it fits tightly. The end of the first piece and the surface of the second piece should be flush.

2. Trim with a sharp chisel until it fits snugly. Fig. 32-4.

ASSEMBLING

1. The rabbet joint is fastened together with nails and glue or screws and glue. Apply glue to the rabbet. Fit the second piece in the rabbet and hold or clamp it securely.

2. Install several nails or screws to fasten the two pieces permanently. Fig. 32-5.

QUESTIONS

1. Describe a rabbet.
2. What are the four steps in making any joint?
3. What should be the depth of a rabbet?
4. Why is it a good idea to use a guide board in cutting a rabbet?
5. Name some ways of assembling a rabbet joint.

Unit 33. MAKING A DADO JOINT

A *dado* is a slot cut *across the grain* of wood. When another piece fits into it, it makes a dado joint. Fig. 33-1 and Fig. 33-2. A *groove* is an opening cut *with the grain*. The back and sides of drawers are joined this way. Because one piece fits into a slot in another piece, it is strong enough even for stair

33-2. Dado-and-rabbet joint. The dado is cut in one piece and the rabbet is cut across the end of the other piece.

33-1. A dado joint.

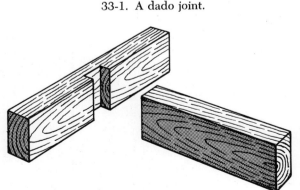

steps. A *cross-lap joint,* which is similar, is made by cutting dadoes of equal width and depth across both pieces that form the joint. Fig. 33-3.

TOOLS

• A *router plane* is a cutting tool made for surfacing the bottom of grooves and dadoes. Fig. 33-4. It consists of a bed with two handles. There are three cutters: two straight cutters ¼ inch and ½ inch, and one V cutter. The cutters can be adjusted to different depths.

• Try square, pencil or knife, back saw, chisel, marking gage, and hand clamps.

LAYOUT

1. Square up the stock. The end

a

33-3. (a) A cross lap. This can be made the same way as a dado joint. Just cut two equal-size dadoes. (b) A cross-lap joint can be made at an angle, as done in making the legs of this typewriter table and chair.

b

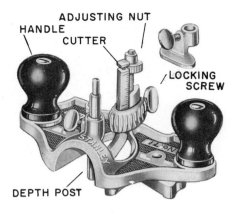

33-4. Parts of a router plane. (Stanley Tools)

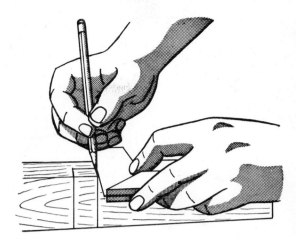

33-6. Marking lines down the edges of the stock.

not exposed can be cut to length.

2. To locate one side of the dado, mark a line across one piece with a try square and a pencil or knife. Fig. 33-5.

33-5. Marking the width using a knife. This is a more accurate method than the one shown in Fig. 32-2.

3. Place the end of the second piece across the first at this line.

4. Mark the width of the dado.

5. Continue the lines down the edges of the first piece. Fig. 33-6.

6. Adjust the marking gage to the depth of the dado. Fig. 33-7. Usually the dado is cut half the thickness of the stock.

7. Draw lines along the edges to show the depth.

CUTTING

1. Fasten the wood in the vise or to the bench top.

2. With a back saw make cuts just inside the layout line in the waste stock.

33-7. Gaging for the depth of the dado.

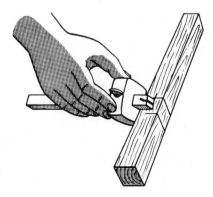

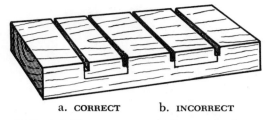

a. CORRECT   b. INCORRECT

33-8. (a) The correct way. The saw kerfs are inside the layout line, in the waste stock. (b) The incorrect way. The saw kerfs are on or outside the layout line.

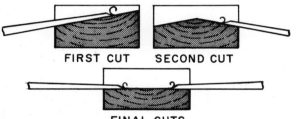

FIRST CUT   SECOND CUT

FINAL CUTS

33-9. Steps in trimming a dado. Work first from one side and then the other.

Fig. 33-8. If you cut outside the line, the joint will be poor. You can do a better job with a guide board.

3. Now make several more saw cuts in the waste stock to the correct depth.

4. Remove the waste stock with a chisel. Chisel from either side to the center with the bevel side of the chisel down. Fig. 33-9. Then turn the chisel around and trim out the rest with the bevel side up. Fig. 33-10. Another

33-10. Trimming a dado or a lap joint with a chisel.

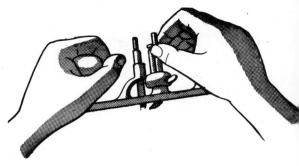

33-11. Adjusting the router plane for the depth of cut.

method is to remove the waste stock with a router plane. Clamp the stock securely to the top of the bench with a good clamp. Select the widest cutter that will fit into the dado. Adjust for a light cut. Fig. 33-11. Hold the plane in both hands and work across the stock with short jerky strokes. Fig. 33-12. Don't try to make the cut too deep at one time. Adjust the plane each time to a slightly deeper cut until the correct depth is reached. Trim out the corners with a chisel.

5. Check the depth of the dado with a combination square or handmade depth gage as shown in Fig. 33-13.

FITTING

1. Hold the second piece over the dado and press the end in. Fig. 33-14.

33-12. Removing the waste stock with a router plane. The work is clamped between the bench stop and the vise dog.

33-13. Using a block of wood with a screw in it as a depth gage for testing a dado.

It should go in with hand pressure.

2. If it is too tight, plane a little off the sides of the second piece until it fits snugly.

ASSEMBLING. Use glue alone or glue and screws or nails. In a fine piece of furniture, only glue is needed. Sometimes screws are added for extra strength. In carpentry, such as building steps, the joint can be nailed.

QUESTIONS

1. What is a dado?
2. How does it differ from a groove?
3. Where is a dado joint used?
4. Describe a router plane.
5. Name some other tools that you need in making a dado joint.
6. Where should the kerf be when cutting a dado?
7. Why should you make several cuts in the waste stock?

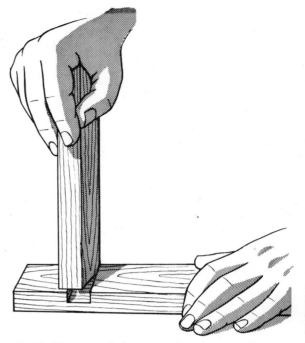

33-14. Fitting a dado joint. The piece should slip in with slight pressure.

8. Describe two ways of removing the waste stock from a dado.
9. How can the depth of a dado be checked?

Unit 34. MAKING A MITER JOINT

A *miter joint* is an angle joint made by cutting the ends of two pieces of stock at equal slants. The most common miter joint is made by cutting each piece at an angle of 45 degrees. When put together, the two pieces make a right angle. Fig. 34-1. A miter joint is used for making picture frames, box and tray corners, bulletin or display boards, and trim for modern cabinets and chests. Fig. 34-2. A miter joint is found at the upper corners of the trim around the doors and windows in some homes. It is also used in house fram-

ing. It is not a strong joint but is used where no end grain should show.

34-1. The miter joint hides the end grain.

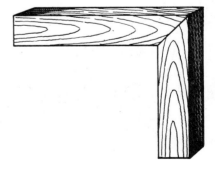

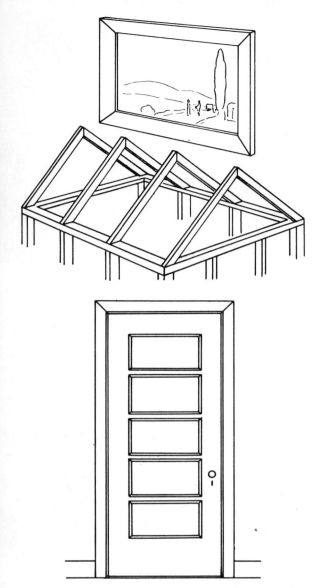

34-2. Common uses of the miter joint. Which one is not cut at 45 degrees?

• Most shops have a *metal miter box,* Fig. 34-3, for cutting a miter and other angles. The miter saw is a large back saw. The base and frame hold the saw in an up-and-down position. You don't have to guide the saw as you move it back and forth. The quadrant is divided in degrees. An index pin drops into a hole for sawing at angles of 12, 22½, 30, 36, and 45 degrees. To cut a four-piece frame, use the saw with the frame set at 45 degrees. If a frame has eight sides, the miters are cut at 22½ degrees.

• A *handmade miter box* is good to have in a home workshop for making a square or 45-degree cut. Fig. 34-4. To make a miter box, choose three pieces of wood about ¾ inch by 4 inches by 6 inches. Fasten them together to make a trough (a U shape). Make a cut at right angles to the sides and two 45-degree angle cuts, one in either direction. Notice that the distance between the 45-degree angle cuts on the outside must equal the width of the box. These cuts can be made on a metal miter box if one is available.

34-4. A miter box can be made by nailing three boards together. Here you see a method of laying out the miter cuts for a 45-degree angle. Measure equal distance from a point to lay out a square. Each rule measures 4⅛ inch.

34-3. Parts of the metal miter box. (Stanley Tools)

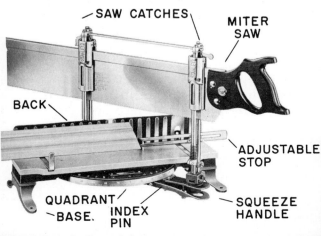

SAW CATCHES

MITER SAW

BACK

ADJUSTABLE STOP

QUADRANT

BASE.

INDEX PIN

SQUEEZE HANDLE

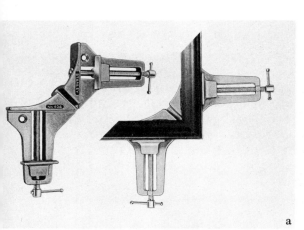

a

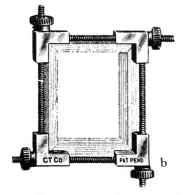

b

34-5. (a) This miter and corner clamp is good for making picture frames because it holds the corners firmly in place as they are glued or fastened together. (b) A four-corner miter frame clamp.

• A *miter-and-corner clamp* is the ideal clamp for assembling frames. This clamp allows you to fasten the corner with the two pieces held firmly in place. Fig. 34-5 (a). If the joint is glued, you can wipe away extra glue easily. If the joint isn't quite perfect, you can true it up with a back saw. A four-corner miter-frame clamp holds all four corners at the same time. Fig. 34-5 (b).
• Back saw, combination square, and pencil.

Making a Layout

1. Mark the length of the stock

LENGTH OF GLASS OR PICTURE

34-6. (a) An attractive picture frame always makes a good project. (b) Laying out a picture frame. The length marked on the outside of the frame is equal to the length of the glass plus twice the width of the stock measured from the rabbet to the outside edge.

along the edge away from you (the back edge).
2. If you are using picture-framing material with a rabbet edge, make the layout as follows:
• Measure the overall size of the glass or the board.
• Measure the width of the framing material from the rabbet edge to the outside. Add twice this measurement to the length of the glass or board.
• Mark the length on all pieces on the back edge.
• If the frame is rectangular in shape, remember to measure the two sides and then the two ends. Make sure both matching pieces are the same length. Fig. 34-6.

123

34-7. Using a metal miter box.

3. If no miter box is used, mark the angle of the joint with a combination square.

CUTTING THE JOINT

1. Hold the stock in the miter box. The back edge of the work is against the back of the saw. Turn the saw 45 degrees to the left and cut the right end. Fig. 34-7. Cut all pieces. When using a metal miter box, put a piece of scrap stock under the work. This will keep the saw from marring the fine wood base. Hold the saw firmly and then release the catches that hold the saw up. Lower the saw slowly until the blade is just outside the layout line. Hold the stock firmly against the back

34-8. Using a homemade miter box to cut a 45-degree angle. Notice that a hand saw with fine teeth is used. A back saw could also be used. This is very satisfactory for doing small jobs around the home.

with one hand. Saw with uniform strokes.

2. Then shift the stock. Turn the saw 45 degrees to the right and cut the left end. Fig. 34-8. Remember, *reverse the saw not the material.* Cut all pieces.

FITTING THE JOINT

1. Place the parts of the frame on a flat bench.
2. Check across the corners with a try square to see that they fit properly.
3. Measure with a rule across the

34-9. Assembling a miter joint by nailing.

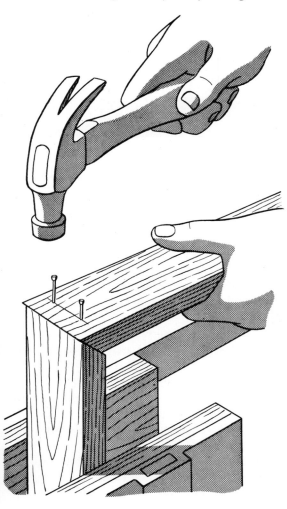

length and width at the corners.

4. If the corner is slightly off, clamp the two pieces in a miter or corner clamp. Then saw through the joint with a very fine back saw.

5. Another method is to plane or sand any high spots to make the corner fit snugly.

Assembling the Joint

1. There are several ways of fastening a miter joint. The simplest is to nail the corner. Fig. 34-9. Drive a nail into the first piece until the point just comes through the wood. Clamp the second piece in a vertical position in a vise. Hold the first piece with the corner slightly over the edge of the second piece. Drive the nail. The second piece will slip into place as the nail is set.

2. Clamp the two pieces in a miter-and-corner clamp. Nail or glue them.

3. Drill or bore a hole at right angles to each miter cut and fit a dowel across the corners.

4. For rough work, the joint can be fastened with corrugated fasteners (wiggle nails) across each corner. See Fig. 30-7.

Questions

1. At what angle are ends usually cut in a miter joint?
2. What are the advantages and disadvantages of this joint?
3. What is a metal miter box?
4. Tell how to make a miter box.
5. Describe making a layout for a picture frame that is 10 by 12 inches. The width of the frame from the rabbet edge is 2 inches.
6. Tell how corners can be strengthened.
7. When can corrugated fasteners be used?

Unit 35. CLAMPING AND GLUING UP STOCK

If the project is small or made of plywood, you probably won't need clamps and glue until you assemble it. However, for larger projects you will have to glue pieces together as you go. For example, you might have to glue stock edge to edge to make the top for a table or chair. Stock may have to be glued face to face to make legs.

Tools and Materials

• *Clamps* are used to hold pieces together:
1. To find out how they fit.
2. To hold them as the glue dries.
3. For installing nails or screws.
4. To do chiseling or planing on them.
• *Hand screws* are used for gluing face to face, for clamping small parts, and for holding work as it is cut or

formed. This clamp can be used on finished surfaces without clamp blocks. The best size has a jaw length of 8 to 12 inches. Fig. 35-1.
• The *C clamp* is used for clamping face to face, for repair work, and for holding parts together. The 6- to 10-inch size is for general use. Fig. 35-2.
• The *bar clamp* is used for large work

35-1. A hand screw

125

TABLE 35-1

FASTENING WOOD WITH ALL TYPES OF GLUE

Glue Type	Room Temperature	How to Prepare	How to Apply	70° Clamping Time	
				Hardwood	Softwood
Liquid Hide	Sets best above 70°. Can be used in colder room if glue is warmer.	Ready to use.	Apply thin coat on both surfaces; let get tacky before joining.	2 hours	3 hours
White Liquid Resin	Any temperature above 60°. But the warmer the better.	Ready to use.	Spread on and clamp at once.	1 hour	1½ hours
Resorcinol	Must be 70° or warmer. Will set faster at 90°.	Mix 3 parts powder to 4 parts liquid catalyst.	Apply thin coat to both surfaces. Use within 8 hours after mixing.	16 hours	16 hours
Powdered Resin	Must be 70° or warmer. Will set faster at 90°.	Mix 2 parts powder with ½ to 1 part water.	Apply thin coat to both surfaces. Use within 4 hours after mixing.	16 hours	16 hours
Powdered Casein	Any temperature above freezing. But the warmer the better.	Stir together equal parts by volume glue and water. Wait 10 minutes and stir again.	Apply thin coat to both surfaces. Use within 8 hours after mixing.	2 hours	3 hours
Flake or Powdered Animal	Must be 70° or warmer. Keep work warm.	For each ounce glue add 1½ ounces water (softwood) or 2 ounces water (hardwood).	Apply heavy coat at 140° to both surfaces. Assembly rapidly.	1 hour	1½ hours

such as gluing stock edge to edge or assembling projects. The common lengths are 3 to 5 feet. Fig. 35-3.

35-2. C clamp.

35-3. Bar clamps.

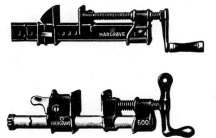

• A *rubber or wooden mallet* is used to strike the wood when assembling projects.

• *Glues* are used to fasten pieces permanently. Table 35-1 describes the common types of glue. Table 35-2 shows the best kinds of glue. A very good all-purpose glue is liquid *resin*. It comes in tubes, squeeze bottles, and cans. The squeeze bottle is best for most projects because it is neat and there is little waste. Fig. 35-4. This glue dries fast. See page 128.

• *Clamp blocks* are small pieces of scrap wood used with bar and C clamps to protect the finished parts of a project.

APPLYING GLUE. Follow these tips in applying all glues:

1. Work at correct temperature. Fig. 35-5, page 128.

TABLE 35-2

WHICH GLUE FOR THE JOB?

	Liquid Hide Glue	Liquid Resin Glue	Resorcinol	Powdered Resin	Powdered Casein	Flake Animal
Especially good for:	First choice for furniture work and wherever a tough, lasting wood-to-wood bond is needed. A favorite for cabinetwork and general wood gluing.	A fine all-around household glue for mending and furniture making and repair. Excellent for model work, paper, leather, and small assemblies.	This is the glue for any work that may be exposed to soaking: outdoor furniture boats, wooden sinks.	Use it for woodworking and general gluing where considerable moisture resistance is wanted.	Will do most woodworking jobs and is especially desirable with oily woods: teak, lemon, yew.	Good for quantity woodworking jobs that justify the time and trouble of mixing and heating the glue.
Not so good for:	Because it is not waterproof, do not use it for outdoor furniture or for boat building.	Not sufficiently moisture-resistant for anything to be exposed to weather. Not so strong and lasting as Liquid Hide Glue for fine furniture work.	Not good for work that must be done at temperatures below 70°. Because of dark color and mixing, not often used unless water-proof quality is needed.	Do not use with oily woods or with joints that are not closely fitted and tightly clamped. Must be mixed for each use.	Not moisture resistant enough for outdoor furniture. Will stain acid woods such as redwood. Must be mixed for each use.	Too much trouble to use for small jobs or most home shop work. Not waterproof.
Advantages:	Very strong because it is raw-hide-tough and does not become brittle. It is easy to use, light in color, resists heat and mold. It has good filling qualities, so gives strenth even in poorly fitted joints.	Always ready to use at any temperature. Nonstaining, clean and white. Quick-setting qualities recommend it for work where good clamping is not possible.	Very strong, as well as waterproof. It works better with poor joints than many glues do.	Very strong, although brittle if joint fits poorly. Light-colored, almost waterproof.	Strong, fairly water-resistant, works in cool locations, fills poor joints well.	Same advantages as Liquid Hide Glue but must be mixed, heated, kept hot, used at high temperatures.
Source:	From animal hides and bones.	From chemicals.	From chemicals.	From chemicals.	From milk curd.	From animal hides and bones.

35-4. A squeeze bottle is an easy and economical way to apply glue.

35-6. When gluing end grain it is a good idea to apply the thin coat of glue first. The end grain will absorb the glue. When applying glue to the rest of the joint, apply a second coat to the end grain. Notice that a brush is used to apply the liquid glue.

2. Apply two coats of glue to end grain. Fig. 35-6.

3. Find the most convenient way to apply the glue. Fig. 35-7.

4. Cover surfaces evenly.

MIXING POWDERED RESIN OR CASEIN GLUES

1. Powdered glues are mixed as needed. Follow directions on the can carefully. Never mix more glue than you can use at one time.

2. Most of these glues are mixed with an equal amount of water.

3. Stir the glue briskly. Then allow

it to stand about 15 minutes.

4. Mix again for about one minute. The glue should be about as thick as whipping cream.

5. Apply the glue with a brush or stick.

MIXING RESORCINOL GLUE

1. This glue comes in two separate cans. One contains the liquid resin and the other the powdered catalyst (a material that makes the glue work better and helps it to harden).

35-5. To do good gluing, both the shop and the glue must be warm. For most gluing the shop must be at least 70 degrees or warmer.

35-7. Applying glue from a tube. This is an especially good way for small projects or repair jobs.

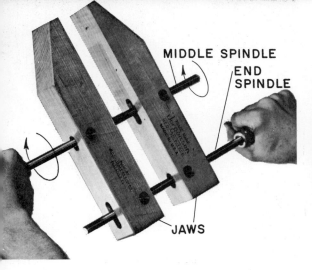

MIDDLE SPINDLE
END SPINDLE
JAWS

35-8. Parts of a hand screw.

35-9. Note that the clamps are fastened from opposite sides.

2. Mix the liquid and the powder in the exact amounts stated on the label. Never mix more than you need for one job.

USING HAND SCREWS

The parts of a hand screw are shown in Fig. 35-8. To adjust a hand screw, grasp the handle of the middle spindle in one hand and the handle of the end spindle in the other. Revolve the spindles at the same time—in one direction to open and in the other to close. If the jaws aren't parallel, adjust one spindle until they are. Always tighten the middle spindle first and then the end spindle. Reverse to remove.

GLUING STOCK EDGE TO EDGE

1. Choose the number of pieces needed to make the larger surface. Use pieces not more than 5 to 6 inches wide.
2. Square up each piece.
3. Arrange the pieces so that:
• The grain runs in the same direction.
• The annular rings at the ends of boards are in opposite directions.
• The grain matches.
4. Mark the matching joints 1-1, 2-2, etc.
5. Test the edge joints to make sure the ends are tight. On long pieces the edges are planed so there is a little opening (about the thickness of paper) near the center.
6. Add dowels or splines if you want a stronger joint. See Unit 31.
7. Choose at least three bar clamps to hold the parts together. There should be a clamp every 10 to 12 inches along the assembly.
8. If the outer edges must be protected, use clamp blocks.
9. If the assembly is wide, put cleats across the ends to keep the surface level.
10. Make a trial assembly to see that everything is all right. Open the bar clamps slightly wider than the assembly. Alternate the clamps—one above, the next below. Fig. 35-9. Tighten the clamps with moderate pressure. Check to make sure the surface is level and the joints are closed.
11. Take the assembly apart.
12. Apply glue to the edges and dowels or splines. Cover the edges but do not put on so much glue that it will squeeze out.
13. Put the joints together quickly.
14. Tighten the clamps a little at a time. If necessary, force the parts together with a rubber mallet.
15. If necessary put cleats across

35-10. When gluing face to face with C clamps, always use clamp blocks.

35-12. Here a project is being assembled. Note the clamp blocks being used to protect the project.

the ends. Wax paper under the cleats will keep them from sticking. Use hand screws or C clamps to hold the cleats.

GLUING STOCK FACE TO FACE

1. Choose pieces to make the correct thickness. For most furniture legs, two pieces glued together are enough.

2. Square up the stock to rough size. This is done so you can see the grain and know how to match the parts.

3. Assemble with the annular rings in opposite direction. Check to make sure the grain matches. Don't put a very light and a very dark piece side by side.

4. Use glue blocks and C clamps or hand screws to hold the parts together. Fig. 35-10. Fig. 35-11.

35-11. The correct and incorrect way of clamping with hand screws. On the left, the clamps are not parallel and therefore will not hold properly.

5. Apply the glue evenly over the surfaces. Clamp together.

ASSEMBLYING A PROJECT. The steps in gluing up a project depend on how difficult it is. For a simple project of two or three pieces, all the gluing is done at the same time. For a more advanced project, such as a small table, the as-

35-13. Checking the project for squareness.

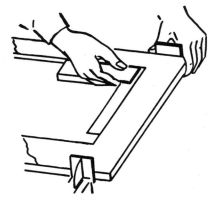

35-14. Checking the project for levelness.

sembling is done in stages as follows:

1. Get all the parts together and check to see that everything is complete.

2. Decide on how the project is to be assembled. Some projects of this kind have four legs and four rails. The best way is to glue the ends together first and then the complete project. Fig. 35-12.

3. Cut clamp blocks to protect the finished wood surface.

4. Select the correct kind and number of clamps.

5. Clamp the parts together to see if they fit. Make sure the parts are square and level. Fig. 35-13. Fig. 35-14. Then take the project apart.

6. Mix the correct kind and amount of glue.

7. Apply the glue with a brush or squeeze bottle. Don't put on too much. Put a little extra glue on end grain.

8. Assemble the first part of the project. Clamp lightly. Then recheck to make sure the parts are square and level. Sometimes you have to shift a clamp or strike a joint with a rubber mallet to bring in into place.

9. Remove excess glue before it gets dry.

10. Allow the first section to dry.

11. Assemble the complete project.

QUESTIONS

1. Name three kinds of clamps.
2. Is it necessary to use small pieces of scrap wood with hand clamps?
3. Which glues are not waterproof?
4. Why is liquid resin a good all-around glue to use in a school shop?
5. What three things must you check for when gluing stock edge to edge?
6. What can be used on the edge of stock to make a stronger joint?
7. Should a small table be glued up all at once? Why?

Unit 36. SANDING STOCK

Sanding is a way of smoothing the surface of stock with an *abrasive* (a hard, sharp material that wears away a softer surface). Abrasive grain is found on sandpaper and in grinding wheels and is used also as a powder. Sanding should never be done in place of cutting. Only a poor or careless worker would try to make sandpaper do what a plane or chisel should do. *Never use sharp tools on a surface after it has been sanded.* The fine abrasive grain left by the sandpaper would dull the tools. Sanding is done (1) on each part after it is cut to final shape and (2) on the whole project after it is put together.

TOOLS AND MATERIALS

• *Sandpaper* is a strong paper with abrasive grain glued on it. There are three common abrasives used:

1. *Flint* is made of soft sandstone. The paper looks light tan on the abrasive side. It is used for hand sanding. It is cheap but does not last long.

2. *Garnet* is a reddish-brown, hard mineral that is excellent for hand sanding. It is also used on power sanders. It will last much longer but costs more.

3. *Aluminum oxide* is a man-made abrasive that is either reddish brown or white. It is used for both hand and power sanding on hardwoods.

The following common sizes of gar-

36-1. Sanding with a handmade sandpaper block.

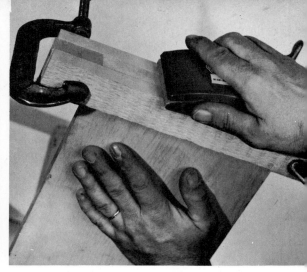

36-3. Sand end grain in one direction. Notice the guide boards clamped over the end to keep the sanding square with the face surface.

net paper are used: 1 or 1½ (40 to 50) for sanding parts with deep tool marks; ½ (50) for all general sanding; 0 (80) for sanding after the project is assembled; 2/0 or 3/0 (100 to 120) for sanding before applying a finish; 4/0 to 6/0 (150 to 180) for sanding finishes. The table on page 134 shows how the common abrasives are graded.

Flint is made in 9- by 10- inch sheets and the other abrasive papers in standard 9- by 11-inch sheets.

• A *sandpaper block* is very helpful. A rectangular block like the one in Fig.

36-2. Using a commercial sandpaper holder.

36-1 is a good one. A piece of leather or heavy felt glued to the base makes a good backing. Putting the sandpaper right over the block is not good. If a sliver of wood gets between the paper and the block, the hard spot can tear the paper or made the sanding uneven.

• A commercial sandpaper holder is shown in Fig. 36-2.

CUTTING OR TEARING SANDPAPER. A piece of sandpaper should be cut into four to six parts for use in hand sanding or on a power sander.

1. Grasp the opposite corners of the paper with the paper side down. Soften the paper by drawing it across the edge of the bench.

2. Fold the paper, sanded side in. Then hold the folded edge over the corner of a bench and tear with a quick jerk.

3. To cut sandpaper, place the paper with the sanded side down on a bench. Place the cutting edge of a saw over the cut line and tear.

4. Always use a piece of sandpaper as small as possible to do the job.

GENERAL SUGGESTIONS

1. Make sure that all cutting is

132

36-4. Sanding with the grain.

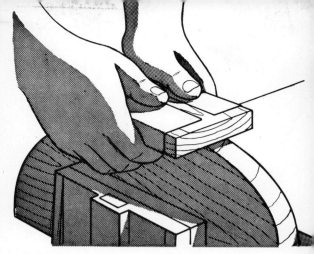

36-6. When sanding a curved edge, sand in one direction with the grain.

finished before you start sanding. Sanding is done to finish the surface, not to shape it.

2. Always sand *with the grain*— never across it.

3. When sanding end grain, always sand in one direction. Fig. 36-3.

4. Apply just enough pressure to make the sandpaper cut. Don't press so hard that it makes scratches.

5. Clean off the sandpaper and the surface often with a brush.

6. Don't sand surfaces that are to be glued.

7. Don't try to sand off pencil or knife marks. Remove them with a plane or scraper.

8. Always brush off the surface after sanding.

SANDING A SURFACE

1. Clamp the stock to the bench or hold it firmly with one hand.

2. Place the sandpaper on a block. Hold the block as shown in Fig. 36-4.

3. Take long strokes, sanding with the grain. Sand evenly from one side to the other. Always hold the block flat on the surface, especially as you near the end.

SANDING AN EDGE

1. Clamp the stock in a vise.

2. Hold the block as shown in Fig. 36-5. Your fingers guide the block and keep it from rocking. Remember that you must sand surfaces square. Fig. 36-6. Unless you are careful you will tend to round all edges.

3. "Break" all edges slightly to pre-

36-5. Sanding an edge. Notice how the sandpaper block is held.

36-7. A dowel rod with sandpaper attached.

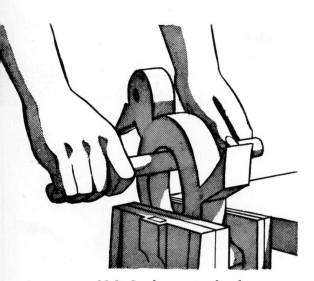

36-8. Sanding an inside edge.

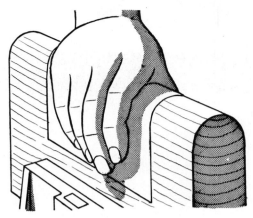

36-9. Sanding a convex surface.

vent splintering. This is done by holding a piece of fine sandpaper in your hand and going over all the sharp edges lightly.

SANDING CURVED SURFACES

1. To sand a concave or inside edge, wrap a piece of sandpaper around a piece of large dowel rod or a round file. Figs. 36-7, 36-8. Twist the tool a little as you sand the surface.

2. For convex surfaces, hold a piece of sandpaper in the palm of your hand Fig. 36-9.

QUESTIONS

1. Can sanding be done in place of cutting?

2. Should you use a chisel on a piece of wood after it has been sanded?

3. Name three kinds of sandpaper or abrasives.

4. What grade of sandpaper would you use for general sanding?

5. Is the size of flint paper the same as other abrasive papers?

6. How do you cut a piece of sandpaper into equal parts?

HOW COMMON ABRASIVES ARE GRADED

Coarseness	Flint (Common Sandpaper)	Garnet (Old Numbers)	Aluminum Oxide (New Numbers)
Very Fine	Extra Fine	8/0 7/0 6/0	240 220
Fine	Fine	5/0 4/0 3/0	180 150 120
Medium	Medium	2/0 0 ½ 1	100 80 50
Coarse	Coarse	1 ½ 2	40 36
Very Coarse	Extra Coarse	2 ½	30

7. Describe the way to make a good sanding block.

8. Should you sand across grain? Why or why not?

9. What must you watch for when sanding an edge?

10. How do you sand an inside edge?

Before applying a finish, make sure your project is really ready for it. A finish will not cover up mistakes. In fact, it tends to show them up! Time spent in preparing the project for finishing is well worth it.

Tools and Materials

• *Shellac sticks* are hard, colored pieces of shellac that become soft when heated. They come in these colors: oak tones of natural, light, medium, golden, and dark; walnut tones of light and dark; mahogany tones of light, medium, and dark. Other colors are transparent (clear), old ivory, white, and cedar.
• *Plastic wood* is a wood paste that comes in such colors as natural, light mahogany, oak, walnut, and mahogany. It is used to fill holes and cracks.
• *Wood dough* is a synthetic (artificial) wood that also can be used for filling holes and cracks. It comes in

37-1. Filling a crack with stick shellac. The alcohol burner is used to heat the end of the stick shellac and the blade of the putty knife. This is a good way to repair dents. It is easy to match the color of the wood.

cedar, walnut, pine, mahogany, fir, and oak.
• *Wood sanding dust* mixed with powdered glue makes a good crack or hole filler. Mix it half and half with water to make a paste.
• A *hand or cabinet scraper* is sometimes used on open-grained wood to get a fine finish.
• *Oxalic-acid crystals* for bleaching can be purchased in any drugstore.
• *Commercial acid bleaches* come from paint or hardware stores.
• Putty knife, Bunsen or alcohol burner, chisel, and scraper.

Repairing or Filling Holes and Cracks

1. If there is a small dent in the wood, allow a wet cloth to cover it for several hours. This will raise the grain. Then sand the surface.
2. For deeper dents, put a heavy, wet cloth over the dent and then apply a hot soldering ccpper or iron to the cloth.
3. Fill all cracks, dents, and nail and screw holes with plastic wood, wood dough, or stick shellac. Fig. 37-1. Clean out the crack or hole carefully. Make sure the wood is dry. To use stick shellac, heat the end over a Bunsen burner until it is soft. Also heat the blade of a putty knife. Then press the shellac into the dent or crack with the knife.
4. Apply enough filler to make it slightly higher than the surface.
5. Sand off when dry until it is smooth and level.

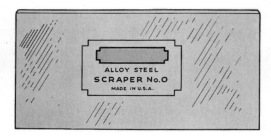

37-2. A hand scraper.

37-3. A cabinet scraper.

37-4. Scraping the surface of wood. This is usually done on open-grained woods such as oak, mahogany, or walnut. Hold the scraper with both hands, at an angle of 50 to 60 degrees to the surface. Turn the blade a little toward the direction of the stroke. Then push or pull the blade.

37-5. Using a two-step commercial bleach. Rubber gloves must be worn to protect the hands.

SCRAPING AND/OR SANDING THE SURFACE

1. On a large piece of furniture made of open-grain wood, scrape the surface with a hand or cabinet scraper. Figs. 37-2, 37-3, 37-4. This must be done before any sanding.

2. Give the project a final sanding with number 2/0 or 3/0 sandpaper.

3. Soften all arrises (corners) by lightly sanding the sharp edges.

BLEACHING WOOD. To get a very light finish, wood must first be bleached. For small projects, use a solution of oxalic-acid crystals mixed in hot water. For larger projects, apply a commercial acid bleach. Always follow the directions given on the container. Fig. 37-5. Bleaching raises wood grain. You must sand again.

QUESTIONS

1. Will a finish cover up any mistakes made in cutting and sanding? What does it do?

2. How should you remove excess glue around joints?

3. What can you use to fill holes?

4. How can you raise a small dent in wood?

5. Why is stick shellac good for filling dents, nail holes, and screw holes?

6. How is bleaching done?

Finishes are applied to wood to protect and beautify the surface. It is important to choose a finish that will suit the project and be easy to apply.

HOW TO SELECT A FINISH

1. For simple outdoor objects such as bird houses and rabbit hutches, apply paint or enamel.

2. For outdoor sports items such as gun stocks, baseball stands, and other game equipment, use a simple penetrating finish (one that soaks into the wood).

3. For indoor novelties, use a simple transparent finish or inside paint or enamel.

4. For furniture and accessories, apply a penetrating finish for simpler pieces or a standard finish for larger furniture.

5. For kitchen items that come in contact with foods such as cutting boards or bowls, use an oil that will not become rancid (spoiled) such as mineral oil.

SIMPLE FINISHES

1. Wax finish.
- Sand the surface of the project and fill all holes.
- Apply a coat of shellac to the surface. See Unit 42.
- Rub down with steel wool.
- Apply a coat of paste wax. Let it dry about ten minutes.
- Rub in with a soft wool rag.

2. Natural finish.
- Apply a coat of boiled (not raw) linseed oil. Use a rag to apply the finish. Wipe it dry.

- Brush on a coat of thin white shellac (two parts shellac and one part alcohol). Allow the surface to dry about twenty-four hours.
- Rub down with fine steel wool.
- Apply a second coat of shellac.
- After the shellac is dry, cover the surface with paste wax.

STANDARD FINISH. While the finishing material may vary, all finishing is done about the same way. There are five or six major steps that must be followed:

1. *Bleaching*. This step is done only if very light finishes are to be applied. For natural and darker finishes, you may skip it.

2. *Staining*. Staining adds the desired color to wood or improves the natural color. For a completely natural finish, staining may not be required. See Unit 40.

3. *Sealing*. It is usually a good idea to seal the stain to prevent bleeding (running of the stain). A *wash coat* (one part shellac to seven parts alcohol) is good for most stains.

4. *Filling*. Paste filler is used on open-grain woods and a liquid filler on other woods. See Unit 41.

5. *Sealing*. A sealer should again be applied over the filler. It should be a commercial sealer or a wash coat of shellac.

6. *Applying a standard finish*. A shellac, varnish, or lacquer finish is applied after sealing. Usually two or more coats are required. Always sand the surface with 5/0 sandpaper after each coat is dry. To give a rubbed finish to varnish, rub on pumice or rottenstone

after the second and third coats. (See Unit 39.) After the second and final coat, all finishes can be made smoother by first rubbing with pumice in oil and then rottenstone in oil, using a felt pad. Always apply a coat of paste wax to protect the final finish. There are many wax finishes on the market that you can use. Consult your instructor.

1. What kind of finish would you choose for a bird house?
2. What should be chosen for projects to be used in the kitchen?
3. Describe the way to apply a wax finish.
4. Tell how to apply a natural finish using boiled linseed oil.
5. Describe the steps for applying a standard finish.
6. Is bleaching done for all standard finishes?

Unit 39. CARE OF FINISHING SUPPLIES

Many different materials are needed in finishing. The kinds you will use on a particular project depend on the finish you will apply. Finishing supplies are difficult to care for. You must help at all times.

GENERAL SUGGESTIONS

• Most finishing supplies catch fire easily. This is one of the great dangers in the shop. Always keep covers on tight and store damp rags in a metal container. There should be a fire extinguisher in the finishing area or room.
• Open the covers of cans carefully so they will not become bent. A tight cover is important if the material is to be kept in good, usable condition.
• Pour out only what you need into a metal or glass container. Certain kinds of paper cups can also be used. Stir the material with a scrap stick of wood.
• Clean out the ridge around the rim of the can and close it tightly. Store the can upside down.
• With wrapping or wax paper, cover the table or surface on which you are going to do the finishing. Old bread wrappers are very good.
• Never pour thinned or mixed finishes back into the original container.

• Use the correct solvents (liquids that can dissolve other substances) for the finishing material.
• Clean your brushes after you use them.
• Store the brushes in the correct solvent.

BRUSHES AND THEIR CARE

• There are many styles, kinds, and grades of brushes. It is always best to choose a good-quality brush. The best all-around brush is made from Chinese boar hair set in rubber. Many good brushes are made from some type of plastic brush hair. A 1- to 3-inch size is best for most general work.

• Always keep brushes in a solvent when not in use:

Varnish brushes in a solution of half turpentine and half varnish.

Paint and stain brushes in one part turpentine and two parts linseed oil.

Shellac brushes in alcohol.

Enamel brushes in a 50/50 mixture of varnish and turpentine.

•Always suspend (hang) brushes in solvent. Never allow the end to rest

138

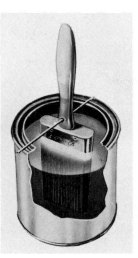

39-1. A method of keeping a brush in good condition.

39-2. Washing a brush. Use a commercial cleaning solvent or a good grade of detergent.

on the bottom of the container. Fig. 39-1. Drill holes in the handles so the brushes hang in the solvent.

- To clean a brush, follow these steps:

Choose the correct solvent. Slosh the brush around in the solvent to remove most of the loose material.

Use your fingers to open the hairs to clean out the waste material. Work the solvent into the area around the handle.

Wipe the brush dry.

Use a commercial cleaning solvent mixed in water or a good grade of detergent. Wash the brush thoroughly. Fig. 39-2.

Dry the brush. Apply a thin coat of petroleum jelly or wrap the brush in wax paper.

FINISHING MATERIALS

- *Benzine* is a colorless liquid made from petroleum. It is used as a solvent and cleaning fluid.
- *Alcohol* is a colorless liquid made from wood drippings or chemicals. It is used as a thinner and solvent for shellac.
- *Turpentine* is made from the resin drippings of pine trees. It is used as a solvent and thinner for varnish, paint, and enamel.
- *Linseed oil* is a yellowish oil pressed from flax seed. It is available both raw and boiled. Boiling improves the drying qualities. It is used in paints, fillers, and stains.
- *Pumice* is a white powder that comes from lava. It is used as a buffing and polishing compound. Use No. 1 for coarse rubbing and No. FF or FFF for fine rubbing.
- *Rottenstone* is a reddish-brown or greyish-black limestone used for smoothing and rubbing. It is finer than pumice.
- *Rubbing oil* is a good grade of petroleum or paraffin oil used with pumice or rottenstone for rubbing down a finish.
- *Steel wool* is very fine steel shavings.

It is used in place of sandpaper for certain finishing operations. Common grains are 000 and 00—very fine, 0—fine, 1 and 2—medium, and 3—coarse.

• *Wet-dry abrasive paper* is waterproof aluminum-oxide paper. Grades 240 to 320 are used with water for sanding between finishing coats.

QUESTIONS

1. In what ways can finishing supplies be dangerous?
2. How can you keep them from being dangerous?
3. What solvent should you use for shellac brushes?
4. What is pumice?
5. What is the finest grade of steel wool?

Unit 40. STAINING WOODS

Staining is done to color a surface and to bring out the natural beauty of fine woods such as walnut and mahogany. It is also done to change the tone or shade of woods, such as making oak a darker color. Staining can make less expensive pines or gums look like hardwood. Gum, for example, can be made to look like mahogany. Staining is the first step in applying most finishes.

KINDS OF STAINS. There are three common kinds of stains. They are named according to the solvent used, *oil, water,* and *spirit* (alcohol). Oil and water stains are easiest to use.

• *Oil stains* come in many different colors. The simplest way to buy them is in ready-mixed cans in colors. Some common colors are light oak, golden oak, dark oak, light maple, dark maple, brown maple, red maple, red mahogany, light walnut, and dark walnut. Oil

40-1. Sponging the surface lightly will raise the grain. After it is sanded, the surface is just right for taking a water stain.

stains can also be made by mixing ground-in-oil pigment or colored powder in a solvent. The solvent can be turpentine, linseed oil, or other light oil. Table 40-1 shows the colors to add to the solvent to make your own stain. Oil stains are easy to apply and have good color. Their chief disadvantages are that they raise the grain and are quite expensive.

• *Water stains* are made by mixing a powder in water. Usually one ounce of powder will make a quart of water stain. Some good things about water stain are that it is cheap, easy to use, gives good clear colors, and penetrates (soaks into the wood) very well.

GENERAL SUGGESTIONS

• Mix enough stain to cover the entire project.
• Try the stain on a piece of scrap wood of the same kind.
• It is better to put on two light coats of stain than one heavy one. It is easier to darken wood than it is to lighten it.
• Wear gloves when using stain.

APPLYING WATER STAIN

1. It is a good idea to sponge the surface lightly with water and then sand slightly with 5/0 sandpaper before applying water stain. Fig. 40-1.

140

40-2. Applying an oil stain.

40-3. Wiping the oil stain lightly with a clean cloth.

Table 40-1

COMMON COLORS IN OIL (TINTING COLORS)				USING COLORS IN OIL FOR FINISHING	
Lt. Yellow	Raw Umber	Orange	Dark Green	White	Use zinc oxide ground in oil
				Golden Oak	Use white zinc tinted with yellow ochre and raw sienna
Medium Yellow	Burnt Umber	Lt. Green	Blue	Light Brown	Use Vandyke brown
				Medium Oak	Use raw sienna and burnt sienna
Raw Sienna	Ochre	Medium Green	Toluidine Red	Dark Brown	Use Vandyke brown and drop black
				Walnut	Use half Vandyke brown and half burnt umber
Burnt Sienna			Deep Red	Black	Use drop black

2. Sponge end grain with water to keep it from darkening too much.

3. Use a large brush or sponge to apply the stain.

4. Apply the stain evenly. Wring out the brush or sponge and wipe off excess stain.

5. Wipe the surface, with the grain, with a clean cloth.

APPLYING OIL STAIN

1. Mix the oil stain in a glass or can.

2. Apply the stain with a good brush.

3. Apply a *thin coat* of linseed oil to end grain first, so it won't soak up too much stain.

4. Dip the brush about one third into the stain. Start at the corners or lower surface and work in and up.

5. Keep the strokes light, brushing the stain evenly. Work with the grain. Fig. 40-2.

6. Begin at an unfinished area and work toward the finished part.

7. Wipe softly with a clean cloth. Fig. 40-3.

8. Allow twenty-four hours to dry before proceeding.

QUESTIONS

1. What does staining do?

2. Name three common kinds of stain.

3. What are the advantages of oil stain?

4. What are the advantages of water stain?

5. Tell how to apply water stain.

6. What should you do to end grain before applying oil stain?

141

Unit 41. APPLYING WOOD FILLERS

Wood fillers are used to fill the pores of most woods and to add beauty to the surface. When the pores are filled, the wood surface is smooth, hard, and ready for any finish you want to apply. Some woods such as ash, hickory, oak, mahogany, and walnut need a paste filler because the surface is covered with millions of small, open pores. Birch, gum, maple, and cherry need only a liquid filler. No filler is required on such woods as pine, poplar, fir, and basswood.

TOOLS AND MATERIALS

• *Paste fillers* are made from ground silicon (sand), linseed oil, turpentine, drier, and coloring. Fillers can be purchased in cans in a natural color. Colors in oil (tinting colors) can be added to get any effect. See Table 40-1 for the correct colors to add to fillers. White lead or zinc also make good wood fillers. These can be used plain or tinted with oil colors.
• *Liquid fillers* can be made by thinning paste fillers with turpentine. There are also ready-made liquid fillers. A

coat of shellac makes a good filler for some woods.
• A stiff brush is needed to apply the paste filler.
• Burlap or coarse rags are needed for removing excess filler.

APPLYING PASTE FILLER

1. Mix the paste filler with turpentine, benzine, or naptha until it is about like heavy cream.
2. Mix the oil color with a little turpentine. Then add this to the filler until you get the color you want.
3. Apply the filler with a stiff brush, rubbing it into the pores. Brush both with and across the grain. Fig. 41-1. Sometimes it works well to rub the filler in with the plam of the hand. Apply a little more filler to end grain.
4. Allow the filler to dry a few minutes until the gloss disappears. This may take as long as 20 minutes.
5. Rub across grain with burlap or coarse cloth to remove excess filler. Fig. 41-2.
6. Wipe very lightly with the grain to make sure the filler is evenly ap-

41-1. Applying a wood filler with a stiff brush. Brush both with and across the grain.

41-2. Rubbing across grain with burlap or coarse cloth to remove excess filler.

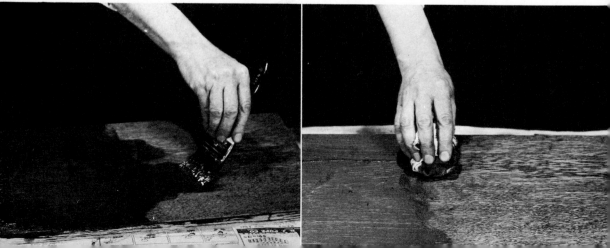

plied. Do not rub, as this removes the filler from the pores.

7. Allow the filler to dry for twenty-four hours.

APPLYING LIQUID FILLER

1. If the filler is made from paste, add turpentine until it is very thin.

2. Apply with a brush and follow the same general procedure as described above.

3. If shellac is used, apply a coat as described in the next unit.

QUESTIONS

1. Why are wood fillers used on wood?
2. Name one kind of wood that requires a paste filler. Name another that requires a liquid filler.
3. Which woods do not require a filler?
4. From what are paste fillers made?
5. How can a paste filler be thinned?
6. How should the excess filler be removed from the surface?

Unit 42. APPLYING A SHELLAC FINISH

Shellac is an easy finish to apply. It dries quickly and is durable (lasts a long time). Because of its drying speed, you can complete the finish in a short time. Shellac is not good if the project will get damp when used. The shellac would become cloudy. Shellac can be used both as the final finish and as a sealer over stain and/or filler. When shellac is used as the finish, it is better over a water stain. Shellac should be applied to knots before painting. Fig. 42-1.

TOOLS AND MATERIALS

• *Shellac* is a thick, yellow material that comes from the lac bug. Most of our shellac comes from India and Thailand. The standard shellac is called a "four-pound cut." This means that there are four pounds of shellac mixed with a gallon of alcohol. Orange shellac is tough and durable but it leaves a yellowish cast on light finishes. White shellac is bleached. It is used on light finishes.

• *Alcohol* is used to thin the shellac and to clean the brushes. Shellac is thinned as follows:

For a wash coat: one part shellac (four-pound cut) to seven parts alcohol.

For first coat: one part shellac to one part alcohol.

For second coat: one part shellac to three-fourths part alcohol.

• A good 1- to 1½-inch brush, a can and a lint-free cloth.

APPLYING THE FIRST COAT. In working with shellac, it is always better to put on several thin coats than one heavy coat.

1. Pour a small amount of shellac into a container. Add an equal amount of alcohol. Stir with a small stick. Don't

42-1. Applying shellac over knots. This prevents the resin in the wood from leaking out and discoloring the paint or enamel.

get the shellac so thin that it runs like water.

2. Dampen a rag with alcohol and lightly wipe the surface to be finished.

3. Dip the brush about 1/3 in the shellac and wipe the sides of the brush on the container.

4. Begin at the center or near the top of a vertical surface and brush toward the edges.

5. Use long, even strokes. *Don't go over the same area twice.* Also, don't use so much shellac that it runs and piles up in small drops.

6. Allow the shellac to dry at least an hour. Four to six hours is better.

7. Clean the brush in alcohol immediately after each use.

APPLYING THE SECOND COAT

1. Sand the surface with steel wool or 5/0 garnet paper. Rub with the grain.

2. Wipe the surface with a clean cloth.

3. Mix and apply the second coat the same way as the first. Remember to *use less alcohol* for the second coat.

4. Allow the shellac to dry. Clean your brush.

COMPLETING THE SHELLAC FINISH

1. If necessary, sand the surface lightly and apply a third coat. Use slightly less alcohol. (Two coats are usually enough.)

2. Rub the surface with fine sandpaper.

3. Clean the surface with a rag dipped in benzine.

4. Allow to dry for 1/2 hour.

5. Apply a coat of good paste wax.

QUESTIONS

1. What are the advantages of shellac?
2. Where does shellac come from?
3. Describe what is meant by a four-pound cut.
4. What is the difference between white shellac and orange shellac?
5. What is the solvent for shellac?
6. Tell how to apply the first coat of shellac.
7. What is the brushing technique in applying shellac?
8. List the common mistakes made in applying a shellac finish.
9. Name some other uses for shellac.

Unit 43. APPLYING A VARNISH FINISH

Varnish is an excellent clear finish. It is sometimes used on high-quality furniture. Varnish is tough and hard. Except for special dull varnish, it dries to a high, mirrorlike gloss. The chief problem is that you can't get a good varnish finish unless conditions are ideal. Varnish dries slowly and collects dust and lint. A poor varnish finish can ruin otherwise good furniture. A good varnish finish, on the other hand, is one of the best.

TOOLS AND MATERIALS

• *Varnish,* which is made from gum, resins, and oils. Turpentine is used to mix or thin it. There are several kinds of varnish. The most common are:

Spar varnish is an extremely tough, hard varnish. It is very good for table tops or other surfaces that may become damp. It is pale golden and colors the wood slightly.

Clear rubbing and polishing varnishes are a variety of clear varnishes

43-1. Applying varnish. Use quite a lot and brush with the wood grain.

43-2. Brush crisscross to level out the varnish.

used mostly for finishing furniture. They are lighter in color than spar or floor varnishes.

Satin, or *dull, varnish* dries dull rather than shiny. It can be used on furniture which shouldn't have a high gloss.

Varnish stain is a finishing material that stains and varnishes a surface at the same time.

You'll find complete directions for applying each type of varnish on the can.

• A good, clean 2- to 3-inch varnish brush.

• A *tack rag*. This is a clean cloth dampened with turpentine to which two or three tablespoons of varnish have been added. The cloth is used to remove dust particles and specks.

• A clean glass or porcelain container.

• Turpentine.

APPLYING THE FIRST COAT

1. Make sure that varnishing is done under the following conditions:

• The room must be clean, free of dust, and well ventilated.

• The temperature must be between 70 and 80 degrees.

• It must not be a humid (damp) day.

• The brush must be perfectly clean and free of dust.

2. Mix the varnish very well in the can and then pour out a small amount into another container. *Never use varnish right from the can* for the first coat. Thin with about ¼ part turpentine.

3. Wipe the surface with a tack rag.

4. Dip the brush about 1/3 into the varnish. Apply with smooth, even strokes.

5. Start at a corner or edge and work toward the center. Fig. 43-1.

6. After one surface is varnished, go over it with the tip of your brush to even the coverage. Criss-cross with the brush to level it out. Fig. 43-2.

7. Allow to dry twenty-four to forty-eight hours in a clean, dry room.

8. Clean the brush with turpentine. Throw the extra varnish away. *Never pour any left over into the can.*

APPLYING THE SECOND COAT

1. Rub the project with 6/0 wet-or-dry sandpaper or 220 to 240 abrasive paper using a felt-back pad.

2. Clean the surface with a tack rag.

3. Apply a second coat of varnish that has not been thinned.

4. To get a mellow, satiny finish, rub the surface lightly with 3/0 steel wool

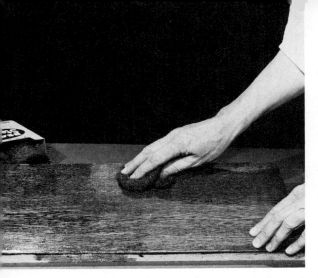

until the entire surface is dulled. Fig. 43-3. Also rub with very fine wet-or-dry abrasive paper.

5. Apply a coat of paste wax. Polish with a soft cloth or felt pad.

QUESTIONS

1. What is the chief problem in applying a good varnish finish?
2. Name three kinds of varnishes.
3. What is a tack rag?
4. What are the conditions for good varnishing?
5. How long must the first varnish coat dry?
6. Describe the way to apply the second coat of varnish.

43-3. Rubbing the varnish surface with steel wool.

Unit 44. APPLYING A PENETRATING FINISH

A *penetrating finish* soaks into the wood. It is excellent yet very simple to apply. You can be sure of good results every time. It is fool proof. It is a good finish to use at home because it is so simple. The final finish looks something like varnish but does not require special care in applying and drying. Penetrating finishes have these merits:

• Only the raw wood needs to be sanded; no sanding between coats.
• The finishing can be done anywhere. No special finishing room is needed.
• The finish can be applied with a rag. No brushes are needed.
• Does not run or show brush marks.
• You can go over the finish at any time.
• Dust does not affect the finish.

"SEALACELL" PROCESS OF WOOD FINISHING

1. Check to see that all surfaces are well sanded. Use 6/0 to 8/0 garnet paper for the final sanding.

2. For a natural finish, apply the first coat with a cloth or brush. Apply it very generously and evenly. Allow it to dry about twelve hours. Then go over the surface with No. 3/0 steel wool.

3. Apply the second coat with a folded soft cloth. Cover the surface. Allow it to dry six to eight hours. Buff again with No. 3/0 steel wool.

4. Apply the third coat as you did the second.

5. You can fill open-grain wood by mixing a natural paste filler with the first coat.

6. You can stain by using ground-in-oil pigments mixed in the first coat. Apply as you would a stain.

7. You can stain and fill in one step by mixing paste filler in the first coat and then adding ground-in-oil pigments to get the color you want.

Penetrating Wood Floor Finish and Wax

1. Select a good grade of penetrating floor finish. Apply one coat with a rag. Allow to dry as specified on the can.
2. Buff the surface with a pad of No. 3/0 steel wool.
3. Apply a second coat of floor finish.
4. Buff the surface again with steel wool.

5. Apply a good coat of paste wax. Wipe with a soft cloth.

Questions

1. What does penetrating mean?
2. What are the advantages of a penetrating finish?
3. Describe the way to apply a Sealacell finish.
4. What other materials can be used for penetrating finish?

Unit 45. APPLYING ENAMEL AND PAINT

If you use inexpensive woods, a paint or colored enamel is often best to decorate and finish it. Painted or enameled projects are gay in color. Designs can be added with decals (pictures pasted on) or contrasting colors. Paint and enamel are both opaque (can't be seen through). Enamel is more difficult to apply but will give a hard, glossy surface. Remember always to follow the directions on the can for mixing, thinning, and drying.

Tools and Materials

• *Enamel* is really a colored varnish. It can be purchased in either high gloss or semi-gloss. Undercoat for enamels comes in white and colors to match the finish coat. Always thin the enamel according to instructions on the can.
• *Paints* are made from white lead, zinc or other oxides, and linseed oil, turpentine, driers, and coloring. There are so many qualities and colors of paints that you can be sure of finding one that exactly suits your needs.
• Use a 1- to 1½-inch brush for small projects and a 2- or 3-inch brush for large areas.

Applying Enamel

1. Check the surface of the wood to see if it is sanded thoroughly. Fill any holes with wood putty. If there are any knots or streaks of sap, cover these with a wash coat of shellac.
2. Open a can of undercoat and mix it well.
3. Brush on the undercoat, applying it much like varnish.
4. Allow it to dry thoroughly. Sand lightly and dust clean.
5. Apply a second coat of undercoat, this time tinting (adding color) the enamel to match the tone of the finished coat. If high-gloss enamels are to be used, apply undercoat made of equal parts of undercoat and the enamel itself.
6. Allow to dry, and sand lightly.
7. Apply the final coat of enamel as it comes from the can.
8. Clean the brush in turpentine.

Applying Paint

1. Make sure the surface of the wood is sanded carefully. Also fill any holes with wood putty. Apply a coat of shellac to knots.

147

2. Select a can of primer (another name for undercoat). Shake it well. Open the can and mix the primer with a stick. If necessary, thin with turpentine.

3. Apply a thin coat of primer with a good brush. Don't make it too heavy. The primer will not completely cover the wood.

4. Allow to dry and sand lightly with 6/0 sandpaper.

5. Apply a second coat of undercoat that matches the color of the final paint job.

6. Apply the final coat just as it comes from the can. Brush out the paint thoroughly on the surface.

QUESTIONS

1. What is the difference between enamel and paint?
2. Which is more difficult to apply?
3. Why should an undercoat be applied before enamel?
4. Will a primer coat cover the wood surface?
5. How should the final coat of paint be applied to a wood surface.?

Unit 46. DECORATING THE SURFACE OF WOOD

The grain of most woods is beautiful. On many articles you won't want to do anything except apply a good finish. For novelty items, however, some other surface decoration may be applied. There are many simple ways of adding decorations. Here are three you might like to try.

WOOD BURNING. A design can be burned into the wood with a *burning tool.* This tool looks like a small soldering iron. An electric unit heats the point of the tool. This hot point will burn a groove. Basswood and poplar are good woods for this because they are light in color and the burning shows up clearly. Most burning tools come with several different points that can be used in the tool so the design can be varied.

1. Transfer the design to the wood surface.

2. Heat the burning tool and try it on a scrap piece of wood. Practice burning straight and curved lines.

3. Place the wood on a bench and sit in a comfortable position.

4. Hold the burning tool like a pencil.

5. Start burning near yourself and work away.

6. For straight lines, use a straight-edge to guide the tool.

7. Steady your hand as you burn a curved line. Fig. 46-1. A little practice is necessary.

8. Work carefully. Make corner

46-1. Using a burning tool to decorate the wood surface or apply a design.

148

lines meet neatly. Try to make the curves smooth.

After the design is completed, the inside or outside can be stained a darker color. The stain won't run because the burning tool has closed the wood pores. However, if you think there is danger of the stain's "bleeding," first apply a thin coat of shellac to the area you don't want darkened.

APPLYING A DECAL. A *decal* is a design or picture on paper that will transfer to a surface and stick fast. You can buy decals in all sizes, shapes, and designs from most hardware, paint, or variety stores. They should be chosen after the project is completed in order to be the right size and shape.

1. Apply a thin coat of shellac to the wood surface.

2. Smooth the shellac surface with fine steel wool.

3. Place the decal in a pan of warm water about 30 seconds.

4. Remove the decal and allow the water to soak into the protective paper. This takes about one minute.

5. Slip about one third of the decal off the protective paper on to one side of the project.

6. Pull the rest of the protective paper off as you hold the decal in place.

7. Use a clean cloth to smooth out the decal. Work from the center out to remove any air bubbles.

8. Cover the decal with varnish or wax. *Never use shellac.*

USING COLOR PENCILS ON WOOD. Certain types of color pencils work well on woods. They can be used to make fine lines, light shadings, or solid masses of color. These color pencils are excellent for applying designs to wooden articles such as plates and trays.

1. Sand the surface of the wood with 3/0 sandpaper. Wipe the surface clean.

2. Transfer the design to the wood as described in Unit 9.

3. Color the design with different color pencils or with one color, whichever you prefer. Carefully add the color to each area. Begin to color around the lines and then fill in the large areas.

4. Apply a coat of clear varnish. Buff with No. 3/0 steel wool.

5. Add a second coat of varnish.

6. Buff and then apply a coat of wax.

QUESTIONS

1. What is a burning tool?
2. What kind of design can be applied with a burning tool?
3. Where can you obtain decals?
4. How can color pencils be used on woods?

Unit 47. INSTALLING CABINET HARDWARE

Cabinet hardware is needed mostly for larger pieces of furniture such as chests, desks, tables, and cabinets. Fig. 47-1. However, some small pieces have hinges, handles, and drawer pulls. Fig. 47-2. Remember that hardware is part of the final trim and should be the proper style. See Unit 49. For example, don't put an Early American drawer pull on a modern table. Hardware stores carry a wide variety of these items. You should choose hardware carefully; know what kind you want before you go to the store. Large cata-

47-1. This modern wall cabinet has two butt hinges and a lock.

logs are available that show every different type of hardware item. Some of the more common ones are mentioned here:

HINGES

• The *butt hinge* is the most common.

47-2. This traditional chest has drawer pulls and side handles that match the style of the furniture.

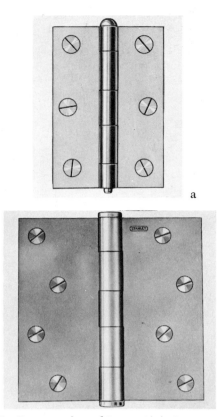

47-3. Common butt hinges: (a) Loose pin hinge. (b) Solid pin hinge.

Fig. 47-3. It is used for hanging most kinds of doors. You can buy this hinge with either a *loose or solid pin*. If a loose pin is used, be sure that the hinge is mounted so the pin won't fall out. One leaf of the butt hinge is fastened to the edge of the door and the other to the edge of the frame. A *gain* (a large groove) must be chiseled out in both the door edge and the edge of the frame. The number and size of hinges depend on the size of the door. A small door of about 18 inches, for example, would probably require only two hinges about 1½ to 2 inches.

• The *surface hinge* is the easiest to use. Fig. 47-4. It can be bought in many different styles such as Early American, modern, and traditional. The surface

150

47-4. Common styles of surface hinges. (Stanley Tools)

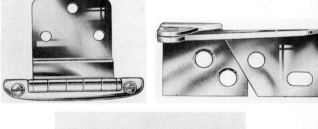

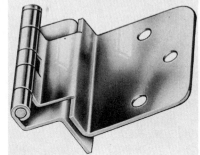

hinge is fastened directly to the front of both door and frame.

47-5. Cabinet hinges. (Stanley Tools)

47-6. Drawer pulls and handles. (Stanley Tools)

• *Cabinet hinges* are used for installing flush doors or for a door with a lip, or overhang. Fig. 47-5. A semi-concealed (partly hidden) cabinet hinge is the most common. To install this, first mark the location for the hinge on the inside of the door and fasten the hinge to the door itself. Then hold the

door with the hinge against the frame. Mark the location of the screws, do the drilling, and install the hinge.

DRAWER PULLS AND HANDLES. Drawer pulls and handles are made in a wide variety of designs. Fig. 47-6. You can find a good-looking handle to

47-7. Catches: (a) Friction. (b) Magnetic. (Stanley Tools).

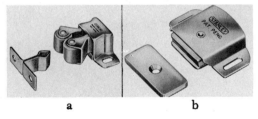

a   b

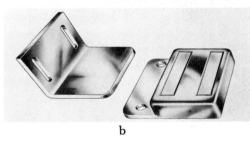

b

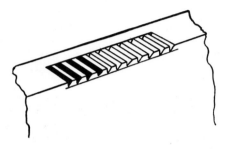

47-8. Gain notches cut with a chisel.

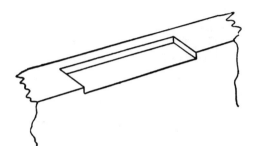

47-9. The gain cut and ready for the hinge.

meet every need, such as a hammered black handle for Early American, a stamped shield and medallion for a traditional design, or a polished brass handle for a modern project. Drawer handles and pulls are sold with screws for installing them, and instructions.

CATCHES. The two most common catches are the *friction catch* for simple kitchen cabinets and the *magnetic catch* often found on fine furniture. Fig. 47-7. There is also a *hook-type catch* for holding one side of a double door closed while the other is pulled open.

OTHER HARDWARE. Some other common items of hardware are cabinet and chest locks and special types of hooks and braces.

INSTALLING A BUTT HINGE.

1. A door is hung with two or three hinges. Select the size and number of hinges according to the size of the door.

2. Fit the door in the opening. Insert small wedges at the bottom and to the right of the door itself.

3. Measure up from the bottom and down from the top, and mark a line showing the location of the hinges.

4. Draw a line across the edges of both door and frame to show the location of the hinges.

5. Place one hinge over the edge of the door and mark how far it extends into the door.

6. Measure the thickness of one leaf of the hinge and set a marking gage to this amount.

7. Draw lines on the door and the frame to show this thickness.

8. Cut the gains for both hinges by hand with a chisel. Figs. 47-8, 47-9.

9. Place the hinges in the gains of the door and drill the pilot holes for the screws. Fasten the hinges in place.

10. Hold the door against the frame and mark the position of one hole in either hinge. Drill the pilot hole and insert one screw in each hinge.

11. Check to see if the door operates correctly. If it does, install the other screws.

INSTALLING A SURFACE HINGE

1. Place the door in the opening.

2. Put wedges at the bottom and at the right of the door.

3. Mark the location of the hinges.

4. Place the door on the bench top. Fasten the hinges to the door itself.

5. Place the door in the opening again with the wedge in its place and install one screw in each hinge.

6. Try the door to see if it works correctly. If it doesn't work right, remove one of the screws and adjust the door until it does.

QUESTIONS

1. What are some common kinds of cabinet hardware?

2. How should a piece of cabinet hardware be chosen?

152

3. Where can you get the cabinet hardware for your project?
4. Name two kinds of butt hinges.
5. Describe a gain.

6. Tell how to install a butt hinge.
7. Describe the way to put on a surface hinge.

Unit 48. WIRING A LAMP

Lamps are very popular. You'll probably make at least one in bench woodwork. However, when the wood base is completed, the lamp is only half finished. You must wire it for electricity and choose a suitable shade. Fig. 48-1. The shade must be the correct size, shape, color, and style to fit the lamp base. See the unit on design, Unit 49. Take the base along when you buy the shade, if possible. Some craftsmen prefer to buy or build the shade first and then design the lamp base. In this way the complete lamp is sure to be better designed.

48-1. Examples of lamp designs. The lamp shades are right for the bases.

TOOLS AND MATERIALS
• Side-cutting pliers, Fig. 48-2, sloyd knife, and screw driver, page 154.
• Materials needed depend somewhat on the design of the lamp.

A *shell socket* with a pull chain or push-through switch. T h e socket case may be metal or plastic. Fig. 48-3 (a and b).

No. 18 lamp cord covered with either rubber or plastic. Choose a color that will go with the lamp.

An *attachment plug* of rubber or plastic. Fig. 48-3 (c).

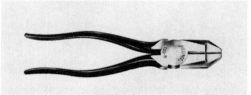

48-2. Side-cutting pliers are used to cut wire.

A piece of ⅛-inch *threaded pipe.* The cap of the socket is threaded with a ⅛-inch pipe thread. On some lamps you'll need a long piece of ⅛-inch pipe with a short threaded section on either end. Fig. 48-3 (d). The pipe goes all the way through the lamp. One end screws into the socket cap and the other end is held in place with a thin nut. Fig. 48-3 (e). On other lamps a small metal plate with a ⅛-inch threaded hole is fastened to the top of the lamp. Then a short piece of ⅛-inch threaded pipe is screwed into the plate and the cap screwed on.

A *threaded brass inlet bushing* should be used if the wire must go through a wood base. Fig. 48-3 (f).

48-3. (a) Pull-chain socket. (b) Push-through socket. (c) Attachment plugs. (d) One-eighth-inch threaded pipe. (e) Thin threaded nut. (f) Threaded brass inlet bushing.

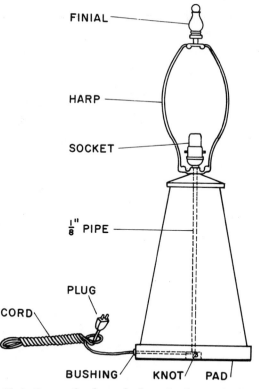

48-4. Parts of a lamp before the lamp shade is attached.

A brass-finish *harp* to hold the lamp shade. Fig. 48-4. The harp may go under the socket or screw on to the outside.

48-5. The correct way of tying an underwriter's knot. One should be tied at both the socket end and the plug end.

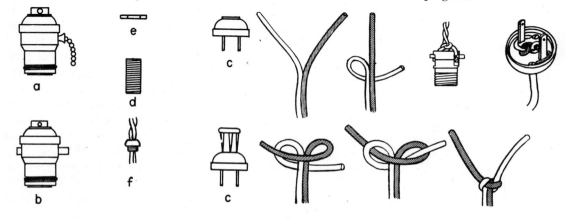

154

A *finial* to decorate the top of the lamp shade.

WIRING THE LAMP

1. Decide on the length of cord you want. Cut the wire to this length.

2. Remove the cap from the shell socket. Press the upper part of the socket near the switch opening. Then the cap will come off. Sometimes, on a plastic shell, the two parts twist apart or there is a brass ring to hold the parts together.

3. Fasten a plate and a short threaded pipe section to the top of the lamp or insert a longer piece of pipe through the lamp. Fasten the brass inlet bushing in the lamp if one is used.

4. Place the under-socket harp over the pipe.

5. Tighten the cap to the end of the pipe.

6. Slide the extension cord through the pipe.

7. Separate the two wires on the lamp end for about 3 inches. Remove the insulation from both wires for about ½ inch.

8. Tie an Underwriter's knot to this end. Fig. 48-5. This knot takes the strain off the terminals (ends).

9. Fasten the end of the wire to the terminal screws of the socket.

10. Close the shell of the socket.

11. Slip the other end of the wire through an attachment ·plug or cap. Separate the wires and remove the insulation. Tie an underwriter's knot and attach the ends of the wires to the terminals.

You may purchase a very simple snap (push-pull) plug. On this one, just slip the double extension-cord wire into the plug and then close the little switch on the plug. No need to separate the wires or strip off the insulation. This will clamp the wires in place and make an electrical contact.

QUESTIONS

1. Name some of the tools you need for wiring a lamp.

2. Describe the things you need for wiring a lamp.

3. What is an underwriter's knot?

4. What safety precautions must be observed in wiring a lamp?

Unit 49. DESIGN IN WOODWORK

What would you look for if you were going to buy a new bicycle? How would you choose among several different makes and models? Would you think about the color, size, and construction? Would you test the seat and the angle of the handlebars—look at the tires and wheels—check to see if the coaster brakes work? You would certainly consider most of these things. Actually, what you'd be doing would be deciding *which design you liked the best*.

In the wood shop you also decide on the *design you like best* when you choose a project. If you design a record shelf, for example, it ought to look good, of course, but it's just as important that it hold the records well. Fig. 49-1. Sometimes a thing looks pretty good but isn't useful; or it might do the job quite well but be made so poorly that it is ugly to look it. Houses, cars, bridges, and all other things must be designed before they can be built. People buy the design they like best,

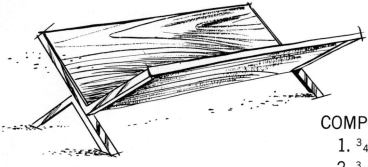

RECORD OR BOOK SHELF

COMPONENT PARTS:
1. $^3_4''$ plywood
2. $^3_4'' \times ^3_4'' \times ^1_8''$ angle aluminum
3. Flat-head screws

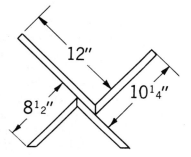

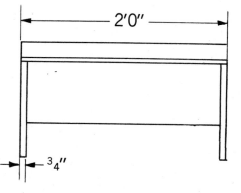

49-1. A simple record shelf made of wood and metal.

that best meets their needs. If you don't like a design, you won't buy it.

49-2, (a) Common kinds of lines. (b) Common shapes.

Design, then, is what a thing looks like and how useful it is. In order to be a good design, an object must be built correctly to be useful and must be beautiful to be pleasing. Design is a part of everything we make and use.

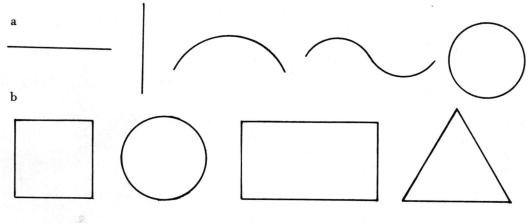

a

b

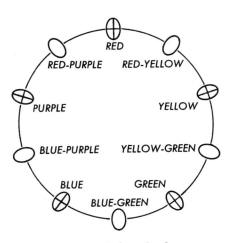

49-3. Color wheel.

49-4. These tables show solid shape, or mass. They have height, width, and length.

It is not something you just study about.

How to choose and make well designed wood projects is not easy. However, studying this unit and looking at well designed wood objects in magazines, books, and stores will be a big help to you. Soon you will begin to get a "feeling" for what is good and be able to discard what is poor.

WHAT MAKES UP DESIGN (THE ELEMENTS OF ART). Design is made up of certain elements:

1. **Line.** All things have line. Fig. 49-2 (a). The four principal lines are *straight, curved, S-shaped, and a circle.* These lines can be combined to make the shape of any object. All things in nature and all things men make are made up of lines.

2. **Shape.** Lines are used to make *shape.* Fig. 49-2 (b). The four basic shapes are *square, round, rectangle,* and *triangle.* We see these shapes, or parts of them, wherever we look.

3. **Color.** There is color in everything. All woods have color. Additional color can be added to a project by applying a stain or a varnish paint. Some colors are warm, such as red, yellow,

and orange. Other colors are cool, such as green, blue, and purple. Look for these on the color wheel. Fig. 49-3.

4. **Solid shape, or mass.** The pieces of wood you work with are solid shapes. Some of these are cubes, rods, rectangles, and bars. When you put these pieces together, they make a larger solid shape, or mass, that can be measured. A table, for example, has height, width, and length. Fig. 49-4.

5. **Tone and texture.** Tone is the light and dark, the shadow and brightness of an object. Texture is the makeup or grain of the material. Each wood has a different texture. Texture gives interest to a surface. There are many ways of adding or increasing texture. Fig. 49-5.

49-5. Tone and texture. The wall shelf is one texture and the other items in the picture show different tones and textures.

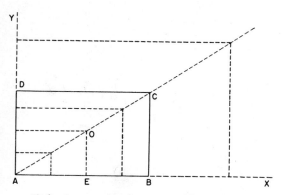

49-6. A way of enlarging a 5 by 8 proportion to whatever size you want for a tray, pin-up board, or picture frame. Make AB eight units long and BC five units long. Then lay off along the line AX any length you want, for example, AE. The distance for width, then, would be EO.

WHAT MAKES A DESIGN GOOD OR PLEASING. It is hard to say exactly what makes one project attractive while another is not. There are many rules about this but rules by themselves don't make good design. Often well designed modern furniture doesn't follow the rules. However, ugly projects are those that violate (break) the basic

49-7. This tray shows good 5 by 8 proportion.

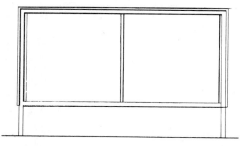

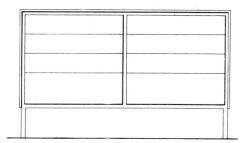

49-8. Dividing space horizontally.

rules of good design. These are the principles:

1. Proportion: The way areas or parts of a project are related to each other. The rectangle has better proportion than the square. This is because the exact relationship between height and width of a rectangle is not easily

49-9. Dividing space vertically.

seen by the eye. The golden oblong is an example of good proportion. This is a rectangle with a proportion of about five to eight. Fig. 49-6. Articles such as serving trays, pin-up boards or picture frames with this proportion are pleasing to look at. Fig. 49-7. To divide this rectangle horizontally into three or four parts, place the largest at the bottom and make each of the next areas smaller. Fig. 49-8. To divide a rectangle into three parts vertically, make the center area largest and the other two of equal size and shape. Fig. 49-9.

Proportion is important when planning a project. For example, the shade for a lamp must be in good proportion to the base. Fig. 49-10. A large shade on a small base would look top-heavy.

2. **Balance:** Makes an article appear equal in weight on both sides. Most things of nature are in balance. If not, they look as if they might tip over. There are two kinds of balance—*formal* and *informal*. An example of formal balance is a teeter totter with two

49-10. A well proportioned lamp shade and base.

children of equal size using it. Two identical lamps on either end of a chest are in formal balance. Fig. 49-11. In

49-11. Good examples of both formal and informal balance. The wall shelves themselves represent formal balance. The things on the top and bottom shelves show informal balance. Those on the middle shelf are in formal balance.

159

49-12. A good example of rhythm. Note how one shape has been repeated.

informal balance things appear to be balanced, or at rest.

3. Rhythm: The repeating of such things as shape, color, or line. Fig. 49-12.

4. Harmony. The way the parts of an object get along together. For example, an Early American leg on a modern table would be out of harmony. A lacy lamp shade would not be in harmony with a heavy lamp base. When the parts go together well, the article has harmony.

5. Emphasis. The center of interest or the point of greatest importance. The point of emphasis catches your eye the first time you look. Sometimes an unusual shape provides the emphasis. Fig.

49-13. Emphasis. The unusual cut of the table, and the legs, make it interesting. The shell is also a point of emphasis.

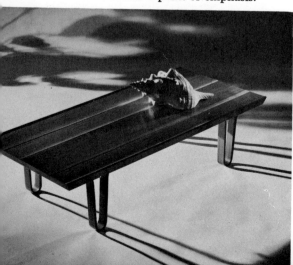

49-13. At other times a beautiful piece of hardware or simply a fine finish is the point of emphasis.

DESIGNING A PROJECT. It would be impossible to tell you everything you need to know in order to design good wood projects. Some of you will have more of a flair for design than others. All of you will learn to appreciate a well designed wood project. You will also learn to recognize poor design. Here are some guides to selecting and designing projects:

1. Make sure the project meets a real need in your life. If it is a stool, for instance, it should be both sturdy and comfortable.

2. The design should be up-to-date. Sometimes old designs are popular and therefore still up-to-date.

3. The object should be made of the best materials for its construction, use, and appearance.

4. The design should carry out the real purpose of the article. Look at the tools used in woodworking. See how well they have been designed to do their jobs.

5. Use really beautiful woods as they are. Don't cover them with paint or a poor finish. Don't try to make woods seem to be what they are not—pine can never look like mahogany.

6. Take time for good construction in making your projects. Make sure your project is assembled with the best methods. Fig. 49-14.

7. Keep your project simple. Don't add a lot of frills.

HOW TO TELL IF A PROJECT IS WELL DESIGNED. Check your project with the following points in mind:

1. **It does its job well.** This is called *function.* A bird house must attract the kind of birds for which it has been built. A shoe rack must be a good shoe

49-14. Interesting table and chair construction. Notice how the joints form a part of the designs.

holder. If your project really does its job, it is worth while.

2. It is interesting. A table lamp might give the proper light for reading but be uninteresting looking. Give a project "personality" and style.

3. It is well made. A chair may be comfortable and attractive but have such poor joints that it comes apart in a short time. Many wood articles have the joint construction exposed to show how well they are made.

4. It makes best use of materials. Most woods are beautiful in the pattern of the grain and the natural color.

49-15. This lawn sign is an example of a novelty item.

Apply a finish that brings out the beauty of the wood. Of course, when a project is made of inexpensive wood, painting or enameling it a gay color adds to its appearance.

BEWARE OF DOG

161

KINDS OF DESIGNS. The things you make in a wood shop can be grouped in this way:

1. **Novelty items.** These projects may be clever and popular without showing good design. For example, you could make elephant book ends or a wall plaque for a good laugh. Fig. 49-15. Such projects don't have lasting value. You would probably use them for awhile and then say, "Well, that was sure a lot of fun to make, but I'm tired of it now." For a good example of this, see Fig. 49-16. Some of the plans in this book are novelties.

2. **Utility projects.** These do a useful job. If they do it well, they are well designed. A fishing lure must be made of the right material and be the correct shape. So must a camp chair, bicycle stand, or sawhorse. This kind of project must be strong and serviceable. Fig. 49-17.

3. **Artistic or decorative projects.** These are such projects as chairs, tables, lamps, and cases. They should be a certain style. The most common styles are modern, or contemporary, Early American, or colonial, and traditional. Fig. 49-18. The design, the kind of wood, the finish, and the hardware make the difference in style.

DESIGNING A PROJECT IN WOODWORK. Let's suppose you decide to build something to hold books. You must first ask yourself how the books can be kept neatly arranged. Books can lie flat, stand upright on edge or end, or lean at an angle. What kind of thing will do this? There is a book trough,

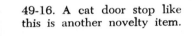

49-16. A cat door stop like this is another novelty item.

49-17. These sawhorses show good design in a utility item. They are strong. They are constructed in such a way that they can easily be taken apart and stored when not in use. They might also be used for the base for a ping-pong table.

49-18. Two small tables: (a) Modern design. (b) Early American design. Both are about the same size and require about the same amount of lumber. The construction is also similar.

book ends, a book rack, book holder, or book case. Perhaps you can think of some others. Next you should know how many and what size books you want to put into it. Most books are about 6½ by 9½ inches in size, although they vary from 5 by 8 inches to 10 by 12 inches and even larger.

Let us say you decide to build a book case. (1) You can make the shelves various distances apart to hold books of different heights. It is a mistake in design to have the shelves equally spaced. (2) Next you must decide on the appearance of the book case and the shape and size of each part. (3) You need to decide how the parts go together, and make a sketch of your project. (4) You might at this point want to build a model. (5) Next comes a working drawing. (6) Last, prepare a bill of materials and write a plan sheet.

QUESTIONS

1. Name three kinds of lines.
2. What are four common shapes?
3. How can you add color to a wood article?
4. What are the proportions of the golden oblong?
5. What is the difference between formal and informal balance?
6. Why shouldn't you put a lamp shade with lace on it on a nautical (sea and ships) lamp?
7. When is a wood project well designed?
8. Can you name some novelty items shown in this book?
9. Tell how you would go about designing a shoe rack.

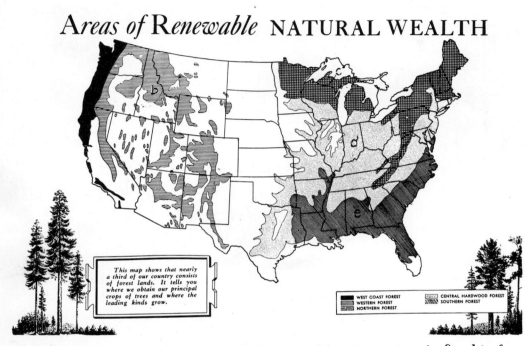

Areas of Renewable NATURAL WEALTH

This map shows that nearly a third of our country consists of forest lands. It tells you where we obtain our principal crops of trees and where the leading kinds grow.

WEST COAST FOREST   CENTRAL HARDWOOD FOREST
WESTERN FOREST   SOUTHERN FOREST
NORTHERN FOREST

50-1. This map shows the forest areas that Mark visited on his trip with his father.

A SURPRISE FOR MARK. Mark Edwards lay on the living room rug in his home in New York City. He was watching his father on television. "Know Your America" was the name of the program. An hour later Mr. Edwards came home.

"I've got a big surprise for you, Mark", he said. "Tomorrow morning I'm taking off on a flying trip. I'm going to do a TV show on what's new in America's forests. Mother and I have talked it over, and we've decided that you can go along."

"Go along! Me? On a plane trip?" Mark was so excited he could hardly talk. "Gee, Dad, where will we go?"

"The trip is all set up. Cameramen are waiting to meet us in five big forest regions. Our first stop is up in the North woods where we'll see real lumberjacks using the latest methods of cutting trees and getting them ready for market. Our last stop will be out on the West Coast."

THE GREAT NORTH WOODS. As their plane took off from New York, Mark's father spread out a map. Fig. 50-1. "The Northern Forest region covers the states from Maine to Minnesota," he said. "We'll visit the New England part. I want to start my show with some pictures showing the history of America's

---

*Used by permission of American Forest Products Industries.

164

forests. You see, lumbering was the first business in America."

The plane touched down on the airport runway. Fred Crane, a cameraman, was there. He had driven up from Boston in his television truck.

"Now, Fred, we want pictures which will show the old and the modern ways of using the forests," said Mr. Edwards as they drove away from the airport. "Let's get the old first."

Fred Crane knew just where to go. First he took them to a very old house. It was made of rough boards and dried mud. It had been rebuilt to show how the early settlers lived. Mark helped the two men take pictures of the wooden churn (for making butter), table, stools and the beds, which were called bunks in the early days. Everything had been made by hand. "The people got nearly everything they needed from the forests, didn't they?" he asked.

Fred Crane nodded. "Yes, even their food. The trees gave them nuts, fruit, and maple sugar. Deer and other animals still get their food from the forest, and so do many people. But today most wood products are made by machines in a factory instead of being made at home by hand."

"Now, Mr. Edwards," he added, "the next thing on my list is the first fire lookout tower built in America."

"Is that one of those tall towers where men watch for forest fires?" asked Mark.

"Yes," said Mr. Crane. "Right close by we can also get pictures of one of the oldest kinds of sawmills. It runs by water wheel, and it cuts logs into boards."

"Most of the trees here are evergreens, aren't they?" asked Mark.

"Yes," his father replied, "they're called softwoods. Most of them keep

THINNING INCREASES GROWTH

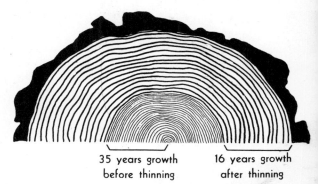

35 years growth before thinning   16 years growth after thinning

50-2. By thinning out the trees through selective cutting, the remaining trees grow faster.

their leaves, or needles, the year around. But we have many fine hardwoods, too."

PULPWOOD LOGGING. The next day they saw trees being cut the modern way. Each wood cutter had a small power saw. In a few seconds the power saw buzzed its way through a tree trunk. The men could make each tree fall exactly where they wanted it.

"A forester has gone ahead of the loggers and marked each tree that is ready for cutting," Mr. Edwards said. "He selects the ones that should be cut now and leaves other trees to grow larger. When they are big enough, they will be cut for lumber. They call this *selective cutting*." Fig. 50-2.

After each tree was cut, the men cut off the limbs. The trunk was sawed into short lengths to be taken to a paper mill. These short logs were called pulpwood.

The next morning, Mark and the men went to a paper mill. The short pulpwood logs entered one end of the mill and came out at the other end as huge rolls of paper.

"Your mill uses a lot of wood," Mark said to the manager. "Aren't you afraid you'll use up all the trees some day?"

"No, Mark; we try to see that that doesn't happen," the manager replied. "Trees have a wonderful way of replacing themselves. See those tall trees out there and the young trees growing close by? The tall trees are parent trees. They drop seed to the ground. The seed grows into young trees. That's how forests go on and on. You know how a farmer grows crop after crop of wheat? Well, you might call it *tree farming* here, because trees grow the same way."

"We'll find out more about that tomorrow, Mark," said Mr. Edwards. "Our next stop is a tree farm in Pennsylvania."

TREE FARMING IN THE CENTRAL HARDWOOD FOREST

"Cock-a-doodle-doooo!"

Mark sat up in bed and rubbed his sleepy eyes. Oh yes! he was on a farm in Pennsylvania. Late last night he and his father had come by plane from Maine. A friendly farmer, Mr. Morgan, and his son, Chuck, had been at the airport to greet them.

"What's a tree farm?" Mark asked Chuck Morgan after breakfast.

"Well, it's some woodland that belongs to somebody—I mean it's not government land—and the owner must take good care of the trees and sell logs or other forest products," said Chuck. "Then the owner has to obey tree-farm rules, too."

"What kind of rules?"

"Well, one is to protect trees from fire. Another is to cut the trees according to a plan so there will always be more crops of trees growing. That means leaving seed trees at harvest time. Let's go out and see the woodlot."

A few minutes later the two boys were riding horses across a meadow toward a grove of trees.

"You don't have many evergreen trees here, do you?" asked Mark.

"No, this is a hardwood forest. Most hardwood trees lose their leaves in the autumn, you know. Before they fall, most of them turn gold, brown, or bright red."

"What do you do with your trees when you harvest them?"

"We sell most of our logs to a sawmill which sells lumber to a factory that makes furniture and toys. We also built our house of the white pine lumber, and used maple for the cabinets and oak for the floors. Then Dad built a machine shed out of poplar. Besides that, we have had plenty of wood for our fireplace."

Mark was amazed. "I knew farmers grew their own food, but I didn't know they could grow their own houses and sheds."

MARK VISITS THE SOUTHERN FOREST

The next day Mark and his father took a plane to Georgia.

"This is a good time to start writing our TV show," said Mr. Edwards. "You can help, Mark. Here's a notebook. I want you to make a list of ways in which forests are important to us. As our trip continues you'll find the list will get longer."

"O.K., Dad."

Forest Products

1. Ships
2. Food
3. Homes
4. Furniture
5. Toys
6. Paper
7. Firewood

The list got longer and longer. Mark called his father to the plane window.

"Look at all the pine trees down there, Dad. Is this the Southern forest?"

"Yes, those are Southern pines. About half the land in the Southern states is covered with trees. Many are pine trees, but some are hardwoods. Trees grow very fast down here. The South has a warm climate and good forest soil. Say, there's something new for your list," he added, pointing to a big building. "That's a rayon plant where wood pulp is made into rayon thread. The thread is sent to another mill where it is woven into rayon cloth. That sport shirt you're wearing may have come from there."

"My shirt! You mean it used to be a tree?"

"Yes, indeed," Mr. Edwards laughed. "Many plastic objects are made from wood, too—such as my fountain pen and your comb."

"Dad, look, isn't that a puff of blue smoke down there? Maybe it's a forest fire!"

"I hope not, but fire is a big problem in all forest regions. We'll visit a modern fire lookout tower tomorrow. So far we've been learning about the good things forests give us. Tomorrow we'll meet one of our worst enemies."

VISITING THE FIRE LOOKOUT. The next morning a new cameraman from Atlanta drove them out through the pine forest.

"I'm taking you to the lookout tower of a paper company," he explained. "Here we are." The truck stopped at the foot of a tall fire tower and Mark and his father and the cameraman climbed to the top.

"What a view!" exclaimed Mr. Edwards. "Look, Mark, you can see for miles in all directions."

"Yes," said the tower man. He picked up his field glasses and took a careful look in all directions. "We keep watch for forest fires day and night. With the help of our maps and instruments, we can figure out exactly where the fire is. With the help of the loggers, the company fire-fighting crew and men who

come from the state fire crews and the neighboring areas, we have any fire out in a hurry. We have only half as many fires as we used to because everyone is so careful—and that means more wood, more jobs, and money for all of us. We all help to *Keep America Green.*"

As they climbed back down from the the fire tower, Mr. Edwards said, "We're flying on to Arkansas tomorrow. We'll get pictures of some man-made forests there."

As their plane landed at an Arkansas airport next day, Mr. Edwards said, "I have a little surprise for you today, Mark. All the trees here were planted by children—some of them younger than you. Twelve years ago this was a bare field. Every year the school children plant a new crop. That's why you see trees of all sizes here. These trees are just about your age, Mark."

A few days later Mark and his father headed west to another great forest region along the coast of Northern California. Some of the biggest and oldest trees in the world grow there. They are called coast redwood.

AMERICA'S WESTERN GIANTS

"Dad! Did you ever see such a big tractor?" exclaimed Mark. "And look at those trucks!"

"Yes, here in the West they use the largest logging machinery in the world," Mr. Edwards replied. "The logs are heavy and very long. Some redwood trees are 2,000 years old. They grow more wood per acre faster than any other tree in America. You could pitch a tent over some of the stumps and live on them, they are so big. Redwoods drop seeds like other trees. New little trees also sprout from the stumps of cut trees. More and more of the redwood forests are being made into tree farms, so we should always have plenty of redwoods."

THE WESTERN FOREST. Mark and his father flew next to the Douglas fir regions that cover the western parts of Oregon and Washington and Northwestern California. During the flight, Mark's father pointed out insect- and disease-damaged areas in the forest below and told Mark about this. Insects and disease together destroy nearly nine times as much standing timber each year as fire does. He also explained that air spraying and prompt harvesting are two of the best ways to control insects and disease. Fig. 50-3.

Mark wrote down what the forests give us in his notebook.

What the Forests Give Us

1. Food, shelter, clothes, and other wood products.
2. Places to go on picnics and for hunting and fishing.
3. Homes and protection for wild animals.
4. Income for people.

When they landed they were met by a cameraman named Chuck Smith.

"Now, I'll show you one company's logging operation," said Mr. Smith. They drove in a car into the mountains. When they met the manager, Mark asked, "Why do the loggers cut a big patch of forest bare at one time? In the other places we visited, they use selective cutting. They just take a tree here and there."

"In the other regions you visited, selective cutting is used because the trees in a stand are of different ages. The old trees are cut and young ones are left to grow. Here in the Douglas fir country, it's different. All trees are about the same age. So they all need to be cut at the same time."

"But if you don't leave any seed trees, how are you going to get another crop of trees to start growing on the big bare spot?"

The manager smiled. He was glad that Mark understood so much about how trees grow and replace themselves. "They *are* leaving seed trees over there, Mark." Fig. 50-4. "See that big block of trees on the ridge just above the bare spot? The wind will blow seeds down the hillside and they will start a thick blanket of new little trees. That's why we call it *block cutting*. A block of seed trees is always left close by for every block of trees which are cut. We have to cut this way to get the new crop of Douglas fir trees to start growing. You see, they need lots more sunlight than other trees do."

"Hey, look, there's a helicopter!"

"Oh yes, that is one of our neighbors. He is planting trees in a brand new way," said the manager. "The helicopter belongs to a company which sows tree seeds by air. A forest fire killed all the seed trees there. The helicopter is wonderful for rough places that are hard to reach.

"Well, that is a new one on me," said Mark's father. "We'll have to have a picture of that."

While Mr. Edwards and Mr. Smith took pictures of the helicopter, Mark started a new page in his notebook.

50-3. Damage to timber is done by fire, wind, insects and disease. As you see, disease and insects enter through fire scars.

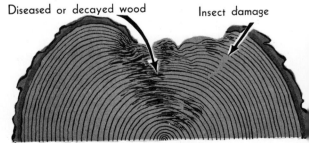

FIRE RUINS TIMBER
Disease and insects enter through fire scars

Diseased or decayed wood

Insect damage

50-4. Here you see young ponderosa pine trees that are the result of careful logging and fire prevention. These young trees grew from seed dropped by larger trees left by loggers for that purpose.

How Trees are Started

1. Nature's ways:
    a. Trees drop seed to the ground.
    b. Sprouts grow up from old tree stumps.
2. Man helps nature by:
    a. Planting seedlings by hand.
    b. Planting seedlings by machine.
    c. Planting seeds by helicopter.

Finally, the manager said, "Well, Mr. Edwards, do you have all the pictures you want? How about a picture of a high climber? You know, the fellow who climbs 170 feet up a Douglas fir tree and cuts the top off. It's something to watch."

"Great!" exclaimed Mark's father. "Just the thing we need to give our television show an exciting finish."

They drove down the winding mountain road. A few minutes later they came to a big opening in the forest where a high climber was just getting ready to top a tree. Only a very skillful man could do it. An unexpected puff of wind at the wrong moment could mean serious injury or even death.

Digging his sharp spurs into the bark, the high climber mounted the tree rapidly. Then, he cut a notch on one side and swiftly and carefully sawed through the trunk from the opposite side. The tree top trembled, leaned, and dropped to earth with a crash. Then the high climber fastened a pulley to the top of the tree trunk. A cable could now be drawn through the pulley and used for dragging heavy logs to the loading point. It would now be called a spar tree.

Mr. Edwards and Mr. Smith caught the exciting scene in pictures. "Well, that does it," said Mr. Edwards. "We've got our show, and I'm sure it's a good one."

The next day Mark and his father

flew back home to New York. As they neared home, Mark read through his notebook and thought of all the things he had learned about the forests. He was sure that this had been the most wonderful trip he could ever take.

QUESTIONS

1. List five forest regions of America.
2. What kind of foods did the early settlers get from trees?
3. What kind of trees are evergreens?
4. What is selective cutting?
5. Tell what tree farming is.
6. List some of the forest products.
7. Tell what a lookout tower is.
8. In what part of the country are the largest logging machines used?
9. What is block cutting?
10. How are new trees started?
11. Tell some of the things Mark learned about forests.

51-1. This western pine is marked with a paint spray gun so the loggers will know it should be cut.

Unit 51. LUMBERING

51-2. The fallers use a power saw to cut down a big ponderosa pine. The cut is being made low on the trunk. This makes the amount of wood loss very small.

Lumber is one of the most useful and many-sided products of the tree. The terms "forest products" and "lumber" mean the same thing to most people. If you ask anyone to name a tree product or something that means the same as wood, the answer is usually "lumber." Lumbering begins in the woods

and forests. About 65 per cent of the nation's lumber comes from privately owned forest lands. Farm woodlots supply another 25 per cent. Public

51-3. This log is swung into position to finish out a load on a truck. The truck will haul it to the mill.

51-4. Unloading fine hardwood logs into the sawmill pond.

lands which are mostly national forests give us the rest.

THE CAMP SITE. Most of the camps are permanently located near large forest areas. Once the camp is located, the necessary roads and buildings are built to provide working and living places for the men.

MARKING THE TREES. Which trees to cut in a timber harvest is not decided by the men who cut them down. Trained foresters do this, and super-

51-5. The man on the carrier signals to the sawyer as the log moves out on the band saw. Soon it will shoot back into the saw. Another piece will be cut. The big logs on the left are waiting to be sawed.

vise the harvest. The forester marks the trees with a spray of white paint. Fig. 51-1. He is careful to leave seed trees and young growing stock for future crops. See page 170.

CUTTING THE TREES DOWN. Trees selected for harvest are cut down by men called *fallers*. These men first cut a notch in the side of the tree toward which the tree is to fall. Then they work in pairs and use crosscut or power saws to cut down the tree close to the ground. Fig. 51-2. All limbs are then removed and the main stem is cut into equal lengths suitable for lumber. They know what lengths to cut it and just how to get the most out of each tree.

TRANSPORTING THE LOGS TO THE MILL. Years ago logs were moved to the nearest river or stream and left there through the winter. In spring, as the water rose, the logs were floated down the river to the mill. Today, however, the logs are dragged either by machines or animals to an open place in the woods. Then they are loaded on trucks or railroad cars. Fig. 51-3. Only in a few areas nowadays are logs floated downstream to the mill. Saw mills are located as close as possible to both the forest and the markets for the finished lumber. River, lake, or tidewater locations are good because the logs can be stored in water until they are ready for

51-6. Using trimmer saws to cut the boards into various lengths of lumber.

51-7. These men are grading the individual boards.

sawing. This soaking protects the wood from insect damage and fire. The water is also a good safe storage place for the lumber. This is called a log pond or mill pond. Fig. 51-4.

CUTTING THE LOGS. In saw mills without a mill pond, the logs are piled in the mill yard. Then they are moved by a crane to a conveyor chain that hauls them into the mill and onto the sawing deck. These logs move sideways, one at a time, to the carrier. One of the most important men in the mill is the *sawyer*. He knows exactly how the lumber should be cut. Fig. 51-5.

The logs are first squared and cut by huge band saws into big pieces called timbers, planks, or boards. Farther along the line, edger saws rip off bark and other rough edges and then cut the boards to standard widths. The boards then move sideways to trimmer saws. Fig. 51-6. These saw the ends square, cut out defects, and saw the boards to length. The size and thick-

ness of the pieces depend on whether the wood is hard or soft. This ends the saw-mill processing.

SEASONING THE LUMBER. The boards move out of the mill on a conveyor. Here trained men grade the boards and sort them according to how they will be used. Fig. 51-7. This lumber is called "green". This refers to the sap moisture in the freshly cut lumber and not to its color. Lumber is then seasoned or dried. The first method is called *air drying*. Fig. 51-8. The lumber is stacked out in the open air or in sheds where it can dry naturally over a period of many months. Many of the softwoods are air-dried. Another method of drying is called *kiln drying*. In this method the lumber is placed in large ovens called kilns, where heat and moisture are carefully controlled. First steam is sprayed on the lumber. Then the kiln is closed and warm air circulated through the lumber. This continues from two to eight weeks, until the moisture content in the lumber is about 6 to 12 per cent. Kiln-dried lumber is

the only kind to buy for making good furniture or for other inside construction.

51-8. Stacks of lumber being air dried in a lumber yard. Pine lumber is stacked at the right. Hardwood lumber is stacked in the distance.

QUESTIONS

1. Who selects the trees to be cut?
2. What is the name given the men who cut the trees?
3. Where are the camp sites located?

4. How are logs taken to the mill?
5. Why are logs kept in the mill pond?
6. Tell about the ways of drying lumber.
7. Which kind of lumber (as to drying) should you choose for most projects?

Unit 52. COMMON WOODS

There are over 1,100 different kinds of trees growing in the United States. About 100 are commercially useful. Only 30 are in common use. You will probably use only eight or ten different kinds of wood in your work in the school shop. All lumber is classified by the tree leaf. These are softwoods and hardwoods. See Unit 50. As you work with woods you will find that many of the softwoods are really harder than some of the hardwoods.

PARTS OF A TREE TRUNK. Fig. 52-1 shows the parts of a tree trunk. The center is called the pith. Around this are annular rings which form the grain of the lumber. The dark rings show the summer growth, when the tree grows slowly; the light rings show the spring growth, when the tree grows rapidly. The darker, center part of the tree around the pith is called the heartwood. The outer, lighter-colored area is called the sapwood, Fig. 52-2. The rays running at tangents from the center, or pith, are called medullar rays. These are very noticeable in some woods (oak, for example). The outside of the tree is the bark.

COMMON KINDS OF WOOD

1. Pine. There are many trees in the pine family. Some of the most common are ponderosa, red, sugar, white, and Idaho. Fig. 52-3. All of these are similar in general appearance but they vary in color, texture, hardness, and working qualities. Most are medium-soft and easy to work. They have a light color and a fairly straight grain. Pine is used in building construction for making doors, frames, siding, paneling, and

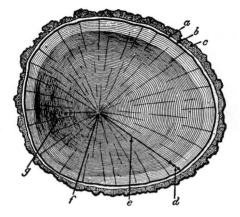

52-1. Cross section of a tree trunk. (a) Cambium. (b) Phloem. (c) Bark. (d) Sapwood. (e) Heartwood. (f) Pitch. (g) Wood ray.

many other things. It is also used for interior woodwork. Fig. 52-4. You will probably use white or ponderosa pine for simple projects.

2. Birch. There are three common kinds of birch: yellow, sweet, and paper. Yellow, the most common, is found mostly in the northeastern and

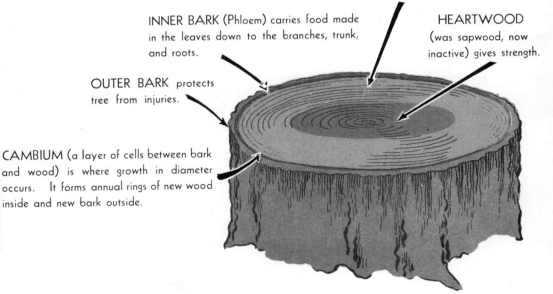

52-2. Here's how the parts of a tree trunk help the tree to grow.

SAPWOOD (Xylem) carries sap from roots to leaves.

INNER BARK (Phloem) carries food made in the leaves down to the branches, trunk, and roots.

HEARTWOOD (was sapwood, now inactive) gives strength.

OUTER BARK protects tree from injuries.

CAMBIUM (a layer of cells between bark and wood) is where growth in diameter occurs. It forms annual rings of new wood inside and new bark outside.

lake states. Fig. 52-5. Yellow and sweet birch grow also along the Appalachian Mountains to northern Georgia. Birch is a hardwood that has fine texture and close grain. The sapwood is light and the heartwood is usually brownish in color. Fig. 52-6. Birch is excellent for

52-3. (a) A map showing where ponderosa pines grow.
(b) Ponderosa pine cones (a softwood).

a

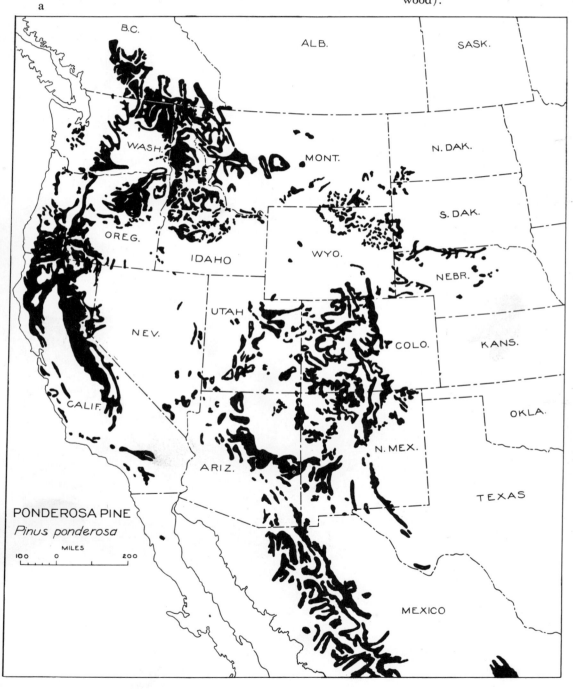

PONDEROSA PINE
Pinus ponderosa

MILES
100   0   200

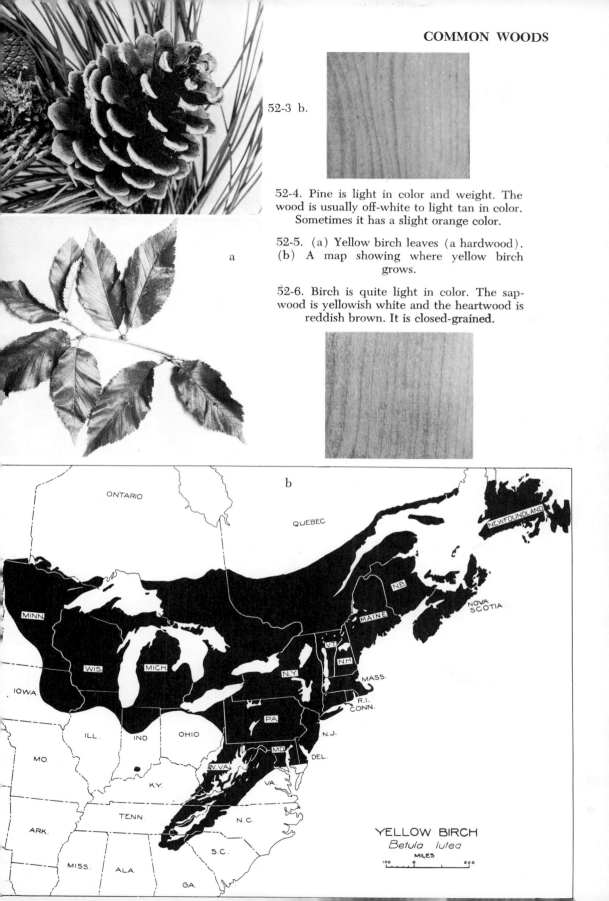

52-3 b.

52-4. Pine is light in color and weight. The wood is usually off-white to light tan in color. Sometimes it has a slight orange color.

52-5. (a) Yellow birch leaves (a hardwood). (b) A map showing where yellow birch grows.

52-6. Birch is quite light in color. The sapwood is yellowish white and the heartwood is reddish brown. It is closed-grained.

a

b

YELLOW BIRCH

Betula lutea

turning because it won't split. It is used a great deal in the manufacture of furniture, for interior trim, and for doors. Birch-veneer plywood is used for flush doors, furniture, radio and television cabinets, aircraft and ship interiors. Birch is finished natural or stained. Sometimes it is stained to resemble mahogany, walnut, or maple.

52-7. Cherry is a light reddish brown in color. It is about as dark as oak. It is closed-grained. Furniture from this wood is often finished deep red.

3. Cherry. Cherry is a medium hardwood that is grown in the forest as a commercial tree. It is *not* the cultivated fruit tree. It is very good for furniture because once dried it won't warp. It is quite easy to work and takes a very beautiful finish. It varies in color from reddish brown in the heartwood to yellow in the sapwood. Cherry has a fairly uniform texture. It is strong, stiff, and moderately hard. Cherry resembles unfinished mahogany. Fig. 52-7. Cherry is used for both modern and Early American, or colonial, furniture and for

novelties and gun stocks. It grows in the eastern half of the United States and Canada.

4. Mahogany. Mahogany is the ideal cabinet wood. It is tough, strong, easy to work, and takes a good polish. It has a deep reddish-brown color which darkens with age. Mahogany comes from many common trees. Genuine mahogany is found primarily in tropical America (Florida, Mexico, and Cuba) and Africa. The mahogany tree may grow as high as 150 feet and as large as 10 to 12 feet in diameter. A wood native to the Philippine Islands is called Philippine mahogany. It looks like real mahogany and is very similar in working qualities and finish. It is a little coarser in texture than real mahogany. A very beautiful wood in its natural state, mahogany varies in color from white to red brown. Fig. 52-8. It is commonly used as veneer on plywoods and is very popular for furniture and for interior trim in homes.

5. Maple. Many kinds of maple grow in the United States. Common ones are sugar maple—also known as hard maple, rock maple and black maple—and red maple, which is also called soft maple, water maple, or swamp maple. Maple lumber comes mostly from the middle Atlantic and lake states. It is a hard, strong wood that resists shock and wear. It varies in color from white to light tan. Fig. 52-9.

52-8. Mahogany is a medium reddish-brown in color. It has open pores and is moderately hard.

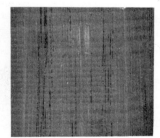

52-9. Maple is light tan in color and very hard. It has a fine texture and grain.

WOODS FOR PROJECTS

Kind	Color	Working Qualities	Weight	Strength	Lasting Qualities (Outside Use)
Hardwoods					
Birch	Lt. Brown	Hard	Heavy	Strong	Fair
Cherry	Dk. Red	Hard	Medium	Strong	Fair
Gum (Red)	Red-Brown	Medium	Medium	Medium	Medium
*Mahogany (Honduras)	Gold-Brown	Easy	Medium	Medium	Good
*Mahogany (Philippine)	Med. Red	Easy	Medium	Medium	Good
Maple, hard	Red-Cream	Hard	Heavy	Strong	Poor
Maple, soft	Red-Brown	Hard	Medium	Strong	Poor
*Oak, red	Flesh-Brown	Hard	Heavy	Strong	Fair
*Oak, white	Grey-Brown	Hard	Heavy	Strong	Fair
Poplar	Yellow	Easy	Medium	Weak	Fair
*Walnut	Dk. Brown	Medium	Heavy	Strong	Good
Softwoods					
Cedar	Red	Medium	Medium	Medium	Good
Fir, Douglas	Orange-Brown	Medium	Medium	Medium	Medium
Pine, Ponderosa	Orange to Red-Brown	Easy	Light	Weak	Poor
Redwood	Dk. Red-Brown	Easy	Light	Medium	Good

Woods marked with (*) are open grain woods and require a paste filler.

It comes in three different grain patterns: straight, birds' eye, and curly. Maple is used mostly for lumber, veneer, and pulpwood. Hard maple has a firm, uniform texture. It is heavy, strong, stiff, hard, and resistant to shock.

6. Oak. There are nine different kinds of white oak commonly used in furniture construction. White oak grows throughout the eastern half of the United States and Canada. Another kind of oak called red has ten varieties

52-10. Oak is open-grained. It ranges in color from light tan to light brown. Red oak is a light reddish brown. The wood is hard and heavy.

that are important. Most red-oak lumber comes from the southern states, southern mountain regions, and the Atlantic coastal plain. White oak has a better color, finer texture, and more interesting grain pattern than red oak. It is considered the best wood for fine furniture. Red oak, because of its slightly reddish tinge and coarser grain, is very good for certain decorative effects. Oak is quarter sawed to show the broad rays, which add to its beauty. The heartwood of white oak is grayish-brown and the sapwood is nearly white. Fig. 52-10. Oak is an open-grained wood. In lumber production oak ranks first among the hardwoods.

7. Poplar. Poplar is classified as a hardwood but is rather soft and easy to work. It is good for beginning woodworking projects. It has a very straight grain and uniform texture. It is light in weight. Fig. 52-11. In commercial furniture manufacture, parts are sometimes made of poplar and stained to look like mahogany. Poplar is some-

52-11. Poplar is the lightest of the woods shown. The sapwood is very white and the heartwood a pale olive to yellow brown.

52-12. Walnut is a beautiful chocolate-brown color. It may have a purplish cast. It has a fine and even texture.

times called the tulip tree because of the tulip-like flowers it bears. It takes a very good finish and is used for house building for both interior and exterior trim. It grows in the northeastern part of the United States from Rhode Island to Michigan and as far south as Georgia and Arkansas.

8. Walnut. Walnut is a beautiful, highly prized native American wood used in better quality furniture. It is moderately hard but still easy to work by hand. This wood takes a beautiful polish. It is often used in gun stocks. It varies in color from rich chocolate brown in the heartwood to creamy white in the sapwood. Fig. 52-12. It has a very attractive grain that takes almost any kind of finish. Besides fine furniture, it is used for veneer, interior

finish, and cabinets. Most black walnut comes from the central states of Missouri, Kansas, Iowa, Illinois, Indiana, Ohio, Kentucky, and Tennessee.

QUESTIONS

1. Name three hardwoods.
2. List five softwoods.
3. Are all softwoods softer than hardwoods? Explain.
4. Is there more than one kind of pine?
5. Name the three common kinds of birch.
6. Name the advantages of cherry.
7. Is mahogany an American wood?
8. Name three different maple grain patterns.
9. What color oak is best for furniture?
10. Why is poplar a good wood for beginning projects?
11. Why is walnut a good wood for gun stocks?

Unit 53. USES OF OUR FOREST PRODUCTS

As you can see from Fig. 53-1, we get many things from the tree besides lumber. These forest products actually come from a crop that is grown over and over again on the same land. In recent years many more uses have been found for tree materials. Can you believe that there are more than 4,500 different uses for wood and wood prod-

ucts? Some of the things that come from trees are described here. Others have already been studied in previous units.

PLYWOOD AND VENEER. Veneer is a thin sheet of wood. There are three common ways of cutting veneer. For fir plywood, the veneer is rotary cut. Fig. 53-2. That is, it is sliced off a log much

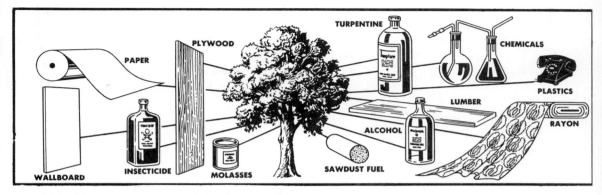

53-1. Here you see many of the things made from a tree.

like paper is unrolled. Most hardwood veneers are made by cutting a log into thin sheets either flat sliced (same as plain sawing) or quarter sliced. Several sheets of veneer are glued together to make *plywood*. Plywood is one of the most useful products of the tree. It is used in all kinds of home construction for floors, roofs, walls, and many other parts. It is also used to make furniture. There are two types of plywood: *Lumber core plywood* has a thick middle layer of solid wood. This is the kind most often used for fine furniture. The other type is *veneer core plywood*. This is made up of several thin layers of veneer. It can have 3, 5, 7, 9, or more plies (layers) depending on the thickness. For example, ¼-inch plywood may have either 3 or 5 plies. The more plies there are, the stiffer the plywood

is and the less likely it is to warp. Plywoods come in standard 4- by 8-foot sheets. There are also smaller sheets such as 3 by 8 feet, 4 by 4 feet, and 4 by 6 feet. There are many special kinds of plywood on which the surface has been decorated or treated in some way. These are usually used for paneling for room interiors or for furniture.

PAPER. We wouldn't have the paper for this book without wood from the forest. Over 60 per cent of all lumber harvested is used to make pulp from which paper is made. In the unit on forest adventures you learned something about the source of lumber for pulp and how paper is made. There are hundreds of paper products that require wood as a basic material.

RAYON. Wood pulp is also used to make rayon fibers. Wood contains cellulose which is one of the main ingredients (parts) of rayon. Many of the things you are now wearing contain materials that came from the forest.

PLASTICS. Another product that comes from the tree is called lignin. This is used to make plastics found everywhere today. We can make "rub-

53-2. This giant lathe peels thin, paper-like sheets of veneer from fir logs. These sheets will be used to make plywood.

181

ber" from wood. This is not really rubber but a product that acts a little like the real thing.

OTHER PRODUCTS. Many other products also come from trees. Today the whole tree, including the branches, bark, and even the sawdust, is used for products that we use every day. Some of these include molasses, turpentine, dyes, drying agents, poisons, and many kinds of chemicals. The tree is a truly great source of the materials we need for living.

Unit 54. EARNING A LIVING IN WOODWORK

Many people earn their living by working on, around, or with woods. Today, well over two million men and women work in occupations that are directly or indirectly related to our forests and the use of lumber. Some men work in the forests cutting trees (see Unit

54-1. A carpenter at work framing a house.

51); other men use the lumber to build homes, barns, boats, and other wood structures. Still others make furniture of wood. Many people find professional careers in woodworking such as teaching woodwork. Here are some of the major occupations:

CARPENTERS. Most of you have watched a *carpenter* build a house. If you have watched a house going up, you know that the carpenter uses all kinds of hand tools, portable (can be carried) power tools, and woodworking machines. Fig. 54-1. Also, you know that he does rough carpentry such as house framing and finished work such as building kitchen cabinets and built-ins. Would you be surprised to learn that carpenters are the largest group of skilled craftsmen in the United States? They are also the largest group of skilled workers in the building trades. Well over 1,200,000 men earn a living as carpenters. Carpenters not only do the original building, but they do repair and maintenance work in homes, stores, hotels, and other large buildings. All kinds of woodworking such as building commercial buildings are done by carpenters.

The hand tools used by carpenters are the same ones you have learned about in this course. The power machinery they use includes the same machines you will learn to use in more advanced woodworking. Carpenters must know how to buy lumber and other building materials, how to plan a building or home, and how to read drawings and prints. They do all the things you have learned in making one of your woodworking projects. Carpenters work out of doors much of the time and must have the strength to handle heavy materials. They are among the better-paid tradesmen.

People become carpenters in one of two ways. Many take courses in car-

54-2. This boat, made of plywood, is the kind that a boat builder must be able to construct.

pentry in a school. Others learn the trade by becoming apprentices. An apprentice is a young man who works with an experienced carpenter, learning the skills of the trade, and then studying carpentry in school or by himself.

PATTERNMAKERS. The *patternmaker* is another skilled worker. He is the man who makes the patterns for metal casting in a foundry. For example, a pattern is needed for casting the body of the plane you use in the shop. A patternmaker is a very skilled woodworker who earns more money than a carpenter. About 15,000 men do this work. Nearly half of them make wood patterns.

BOATBUILDERS. If you live near water, especially large lakes or the ocean, you have seen boat builders at work. Fig. 54-2. Here, too, is a more specialized woodworker. The *boatbuilder* must thoroughly understand boat construc-

54-3. An expert applying a fine finish on furniture.

tion and must know how to select and shape woods properly for use in water.

OCCUPATIONS IN THE FURNITURE INDUSTRY. Many people earn a living in the furniture industry but only a few of them are skilled. Most furniture workers run a single machine and do just one small task or make one small part. Other men are *furniture finishers* who apply the finish to the wood furniture. Fig. 54-3. Every big furniture store must employ a few skilled *cabinet makers* and furniture finishers to

54-4. A skilled cabinet maker at work in a furniture factory.

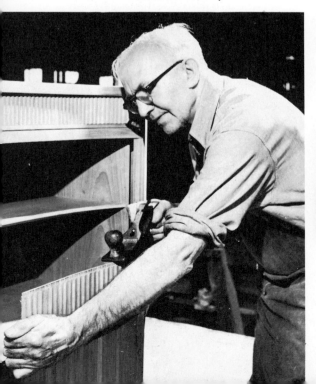

repair broken or damaged furniture. Fig. 54-4. Every furniture factory employs skilled cabinet makers.

PROFESSIONS IN WOODWORKING. Many woodworking occupations require a college degree. Forestry, for example, is one area that is becoming more and more important. There are over 17,000 professional *foresters* who work in the forests or in closely related fields. Foresters do many things. They mark timber, make rain surveys of the forests, do conservation work, and help protect forests from fire, disease, and insects. A forester must have a four-year college degree. He has to work out of doors much of the time. He may work for the United States government or private industry.

There are about 30,000 *industrial-arts teachers* in woodworking. They must know how to use all types of hand and power tools. Their knowledge of the entire field must be complete. Your teacher will tell you more about his work. There are men who work in *research* and *wood technology*. These men must have a degree in chemistry or chemical engineering. A very small number of men work as *furniture designers*. They plan and design the furniture built in factories. *Architects* plan buildings and homes. They must have a college degree and know much about woods and construction.

QUESTIONS

1. What does a carpenter do?
2. About how many carpenters are there in the United States?
3. How can you learn to become a carpenter?
4. What is an apprentice?
5. Tell what a patternmaker does.
6. Are there many cabinet makers in a furniture factory? Where else are they employed?
7. Tell about some of the professions in which a knowledge of wood is important.

On the following pages you will find drawings and photographs that will help you plan twenty-nine projects in woodworking. Perhaps you can select one that will give you a good start in your course, and then later on find time to do others as you progress.

These plans are not the only ones you can use. They are merely examples of the kinds of drawings you will need and how a project should look when it is complete.

We are all different. Some of you will want to "test yourselves" by finding out just what kind of work you can do with a very simple article such as the duck toy or the jar opener. Others may have a home background in woodwork and can begin with such a project as the magazine rack.

OTHER SOURCES FOR PROJECT IDEAS. Later on your instructor may ask you to look for ideas in magazines, at stores, in homes, or in catalogs that will help you decide what to make next.

Things you can make for yourself and a young brother.

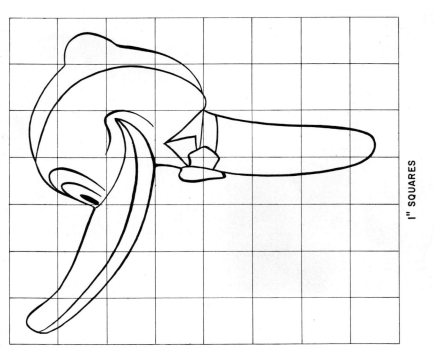

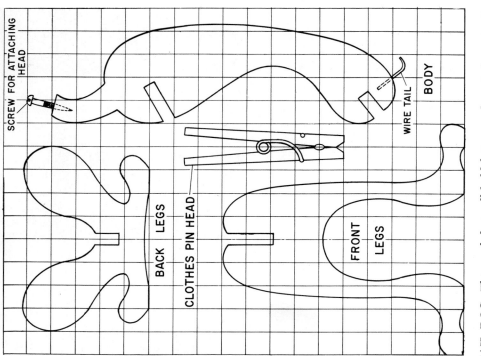

BACK LEGS

CLOTHES PIN HEAD

SCREW FOR ATTACHING HEAD

WIRE TAIL

BODY

FRONT LEGS

MAIL DOG: This mail dog will hold letters and reminder notes that need to be taken care of. Use a clothespin for the head.

1" SQUARES

RING THE DUCK: To the neck of the duck tie a piece of string that is 12 inches long. Attach a rubber jar ring to the other end. How often can you get the ring on the end of the duck's bill?

186

RING THE DUCK

MAIL DOG

JAR OPENER: Make this opener of plywood that is at least ½ inch thick. Taper the opening just a little so it will fit the jar cover.

JAR OPENER

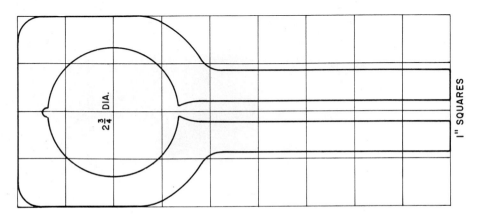

2¾ DIA.

1" SQUARES

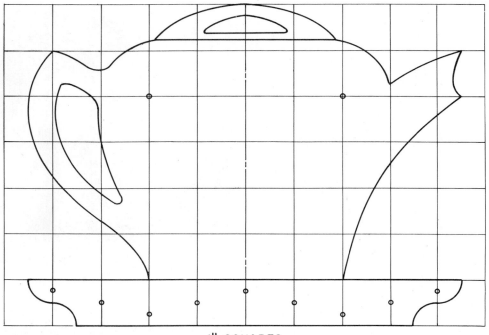

I" SQUARES

HOT-PAD AND SEWING TOOL HOLDER: This holder can be made of solid stock or plywood. The holders are cup hooks. Use as many as you want.

HOT PAD AND SEWING-TOOL HOLDER

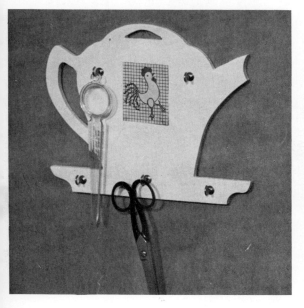

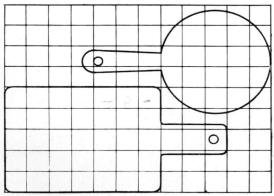

CUTTING BOARD AND SERVING PADDLES: Ideas for a cutting board and serving paddles. These are always useful for cutting food and for serving snacks.

CUTTING BOARD AND PADDLE

MAGAZINE RACK: This magazine rack and the other simple projects are assembled by gluing and nailing. You can paint or enamel them.

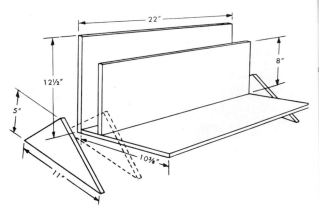

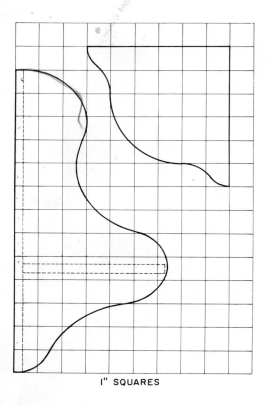

1" SQUARES

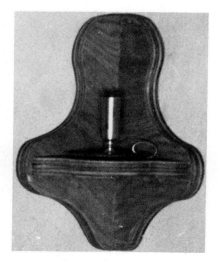

CORNER SHELF

CORNER SHELF: You can make this corner shelf any size by enlarging it. This one is made for miniatures (small-scale models).

DART BOARD AND DARTS: Make the board of fiberboard. The darts are pine or other softwood. The darts must be carefully made so they will be well balanced. You can draw the target on the board itself or on a cardboard glued to the fiberboard.

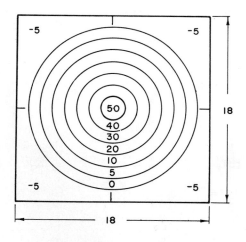

MAKE VANES OF THIN PLASTIC OR VENEER

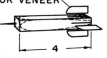

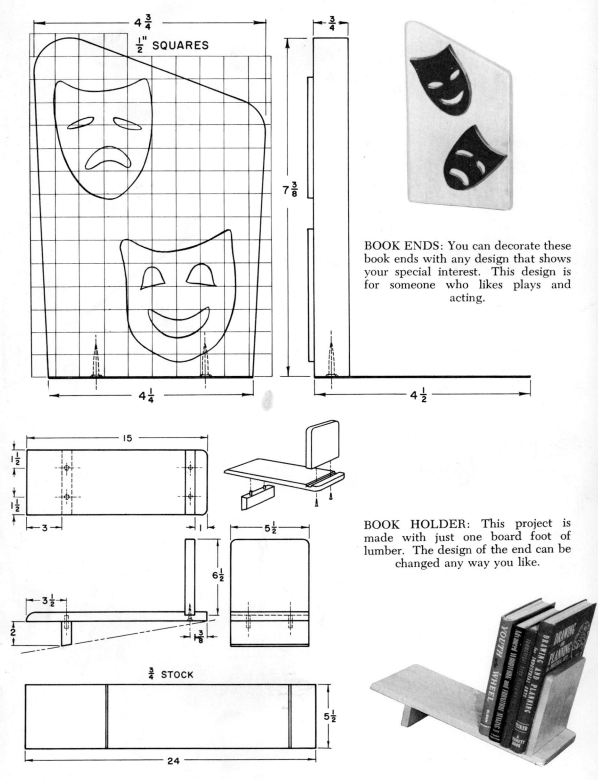

4 ¾

½" SQUARES

¾

7 ⅜

4 ¼

4 ½

BOOK ENDS: You can decorate these book ends with any design that shows your special interest. This design is for someone who likes plays and acting.

15

1 ½

1 ½

3

1

5 ½

6 ½

3 ½

2

⅜

¾ STOCK

5 ½

24

BOOK HOLDER: This project is made with just one board foot of lumber. The design of the end can be changed any way you like.

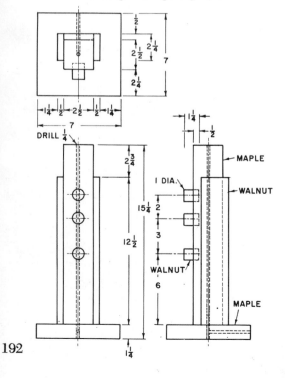

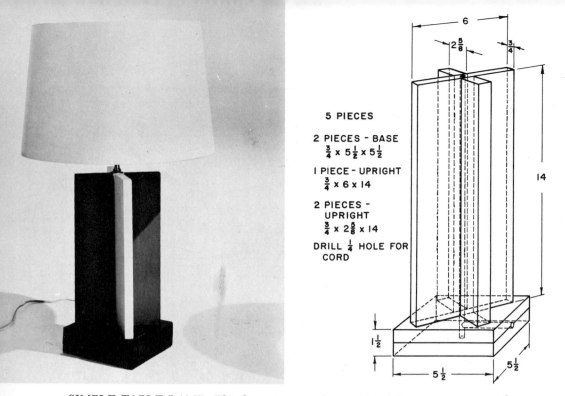

5 PIECES

2 PIECES - BASE
$\frac{3}{4}$ x $5\frac{1}{2}$ x $5\frac{1}{2}$

I PIECE - UPRIGHT
$\frac{3}{4}$ x 6 x 14

**2 PIECES -
UPRIGHT**
$\frac{3}{4}$ x $2\frac{5}{8}$ x 14

**DRILL $\frac{1}{4}$ HOLE FOR
CORD**

SIMPLE TABLE LAMP: This lamp is a good example of how attractive simple things can be. The lamp base is made of two square pieces of stock and three rectangular shapes. Assembling and finishing are very important.

MODERN TABLE LAMP: A table lamp designed to give good light for reading. It's a good project for those who have had some building experience.

192

DACHSHUND TIE RACK

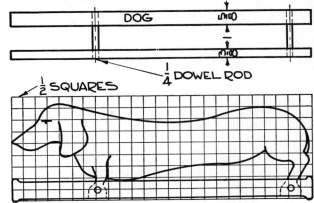

DACHSHUND TIE RACK

DACHSHUND TIE RACK: Here is a project that anyone will like and yet it is very simple to make. It can be cut out with a coping saw or jig saw and the rack itself made in the shape of a long bone. To give character to your dog, you can shape the eyes, ears, and tail with a gouge, although these marks can be painted on also. This one was made of pine.

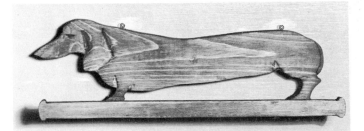

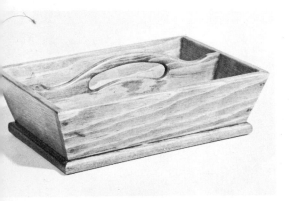

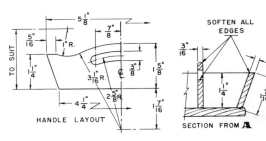

PINE TRAY: This tray can be used for napkins or for serving food such as crackers. The handle section can be cut on the jig saw.

193

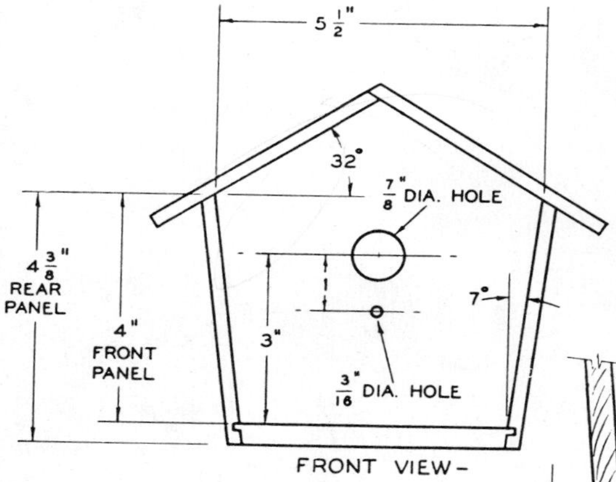
5 1/2"
32°
7/8" DIA. HOLE
4 3/8" REAR PANEL
4" FRONT PANEL
3"
7°
3/16" DIA. HOLE
FRONT VIEW-

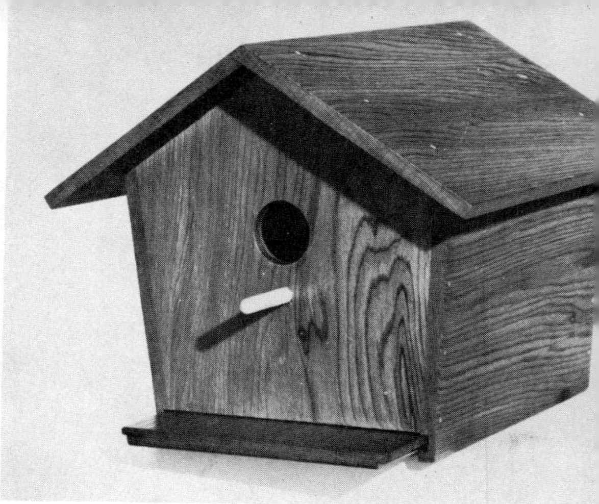

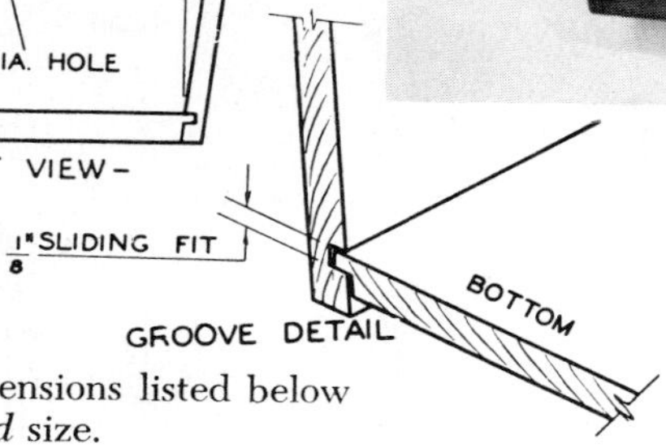
1/8" SLIDING FIT
BOTTOM
GROOVE DETAIL

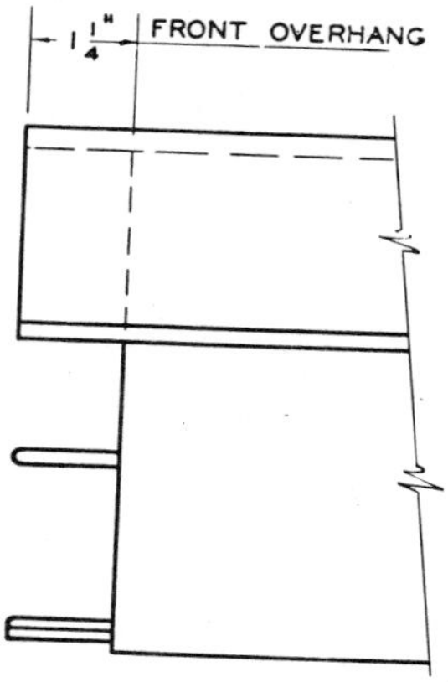
1 1/4" FRONT OVERHANG

IMPORTANT: All dimensions listed below are *finished* size.

BILL OF MATERIALS

No. of Pieces	*Part Name*	*Thick-ness*	*Width*	*Length*	*Wood*
1	Front	¼″	5½″	5¾″	redwood or pine
1	Back	¼″	5½″	6⅛″	redwood or pine
2	Sides	¼″	4⅜″	6″	redwood or pine
1	Roof Piece	¼″	4⅜″	8″	redwood or pine
1	Roof Piece	¼″	4⅝″	8″	redwood or pine
1	Bottom	¼″	4¾″	7″	redwood or pine
1	Perch	3/16″		1½″	hardwood dowel

No. 16 x ¾″ wire brads No. 16 x ½″ wire brads

BIRD HOUSE: The bill of materials shows the sizes for each part. The bottom can be nailed on, instead of removable as shown. (Atlas Press Co.)

TRICYCLE CART:

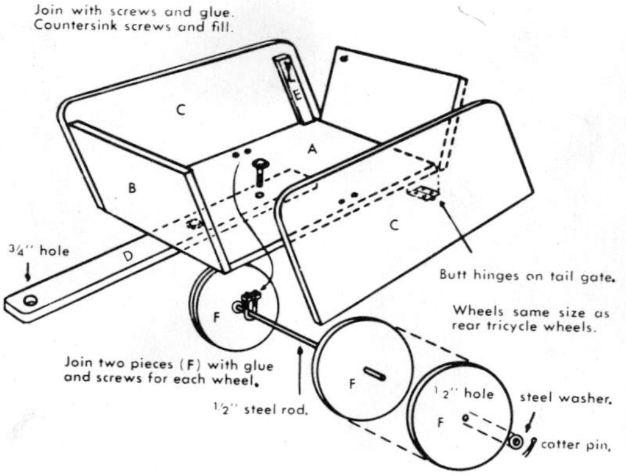
Join with screws and glue.
Countersink screws and fill.
C
E
A
B
C
D
3/4" hole
Butt hinges on tail gate.
Wheels same size as rear tricycle wheels.
F
Join two pieces (F) with glue and screws for each wheel.
1/2" steel rod.
1/2" hole
steel washer.
cotter pin.

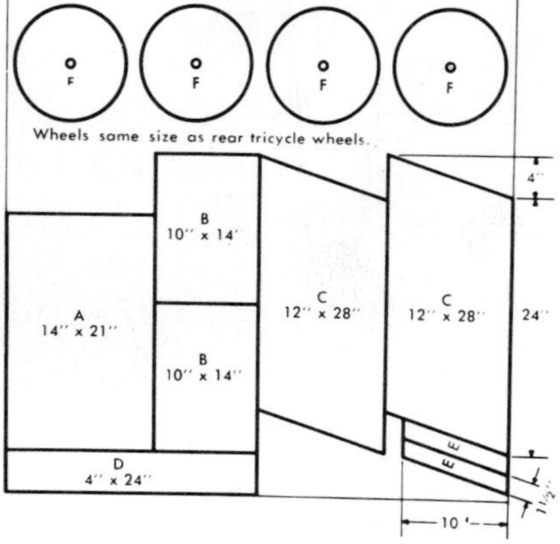
F
Wheels same size as rear tricycle wheels.
A 14" x 21"
B 10" x 14"
B 10" x 14"
C 12" x 28"
C 12" x 28"
D 4" x 24"
E E
4"
24"
1 1/2"
10"

TRICYCLE CART: This cart would make a wonderful present for a younger brother or sister. It is made of plywood. The wheels can be homemade or you can buy them.

TULIP KNIFE BOX: This is really a small plywood box with a handle divider down the middle. The box can be used for holding table silver, letters, papers, or other things.

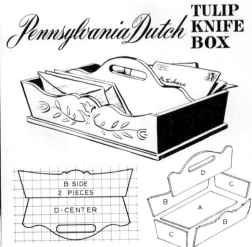

TULIP KNIFE BOX

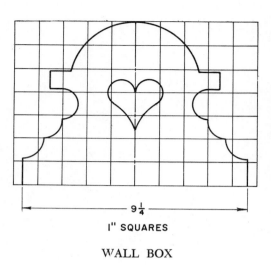

I" SQUARES

WALL BOX

WALL BOX: This wall decoration is similar to a salt box of colonial times. It can be used to store odds and ends. (Reprinted by permission of *Woman's Day* Magazine, February, 1954.)

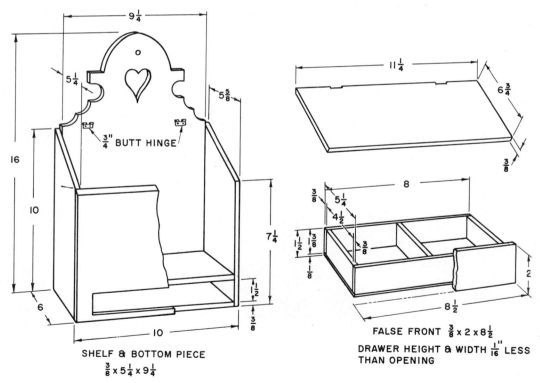

BUTT HINGE

SHELF & BOTTOM PIECE
$\frac{3}{8} \times 5\frac{1}{4} \times 9\frac{1}{4}$

FALSE FRONT $\frac{3}{8} \times 2 \times 8\frac{1}{2}$

DRAWER HEIGHT & WIDTH $\frac{1}{16}$" LESS THAN OPENING

196

PORTABLE HOLDER

PORTABLE HOLDER: This Early American portable holder can be used in almost every room in the house. It might hold books or knick knacks. (Reprinted by permission of *Woman's Day* Magazine, February, 1954.)

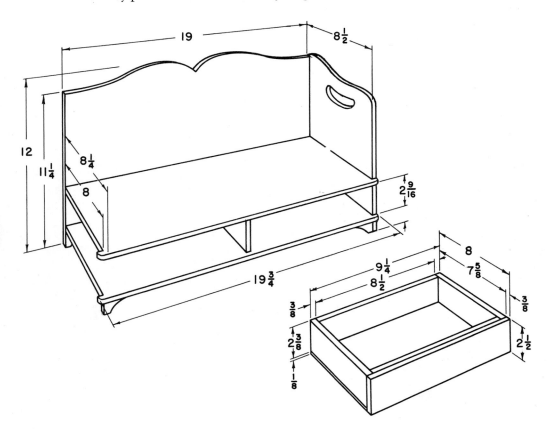

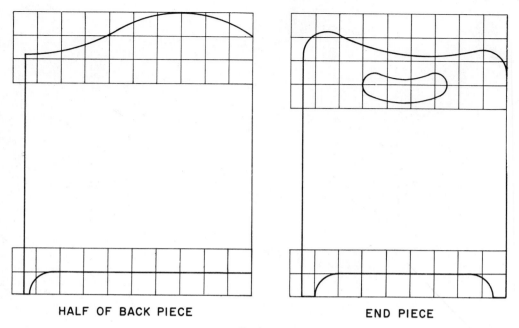

HALF OF BACK PIECE   END PIECE

1" SQUARES

MEMO ROLL HOLDER: Your notes are always ready when you jot them down on a roll of paper. The dip in the sides will hold a pencil.

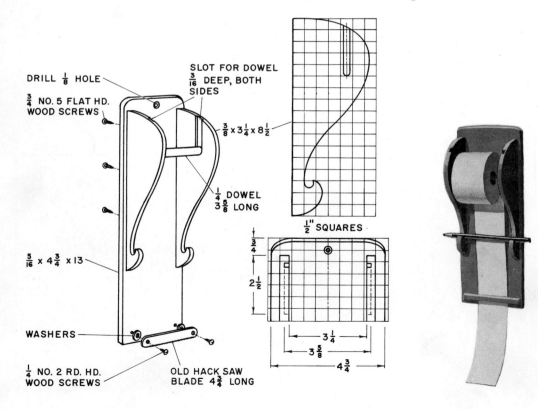

DRILL $\frac{1}{8}$ HOLE

$\frac{3}{4}$ NO. 5 FLAT HD. WOOD SCREWS

SLOT FOR DOWEL $\frac{3}{16}$ DEEP, BOTH SIDES

$\frac{3}{8}$ x $3\frac{1}{4}$ x $8\frac{1}{2}$

$\frac{1}{4}$ DOWEL $3\frac{5}{8}$ LONG

$\frac{1}{2}$" SQUARES

$\frac{5}{16}$ x $4\frac{3}{4}$ x 13

$\frac{3}{4}$

$2\frac{1}{2}$

WASHERS

$\frac{1}{4}$ NO. 2 RD. HD. WOOD SCREWS

OLD HACK SAW BLADE $4\frac{3}{4}$ LONG

$3\frac{1}{4}$

$3\frac{5}{8}$

$4\frac{3}{4}$

198

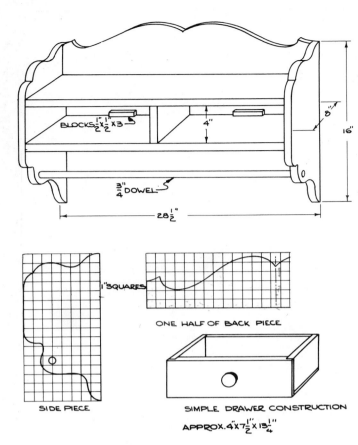

BLOCKS $\frac{1}{2}$" x $\frac{1}{2}$" X 3

4"

8"

16"

$\frac{3}{4}$" DOWEL

28$\frac{1}{2}$"

1" SQUARES

ONE HALF OF BACK PIECE

SIDE PIECE

SIMPLE DRAWER CONSTRUCTION
APPROX. 4" X 7$\frac{1}{2}$" X 13$\frac{1}{4}$"

TOWEL RACK: Just the thing for a bathroom. The small drawers can be used to store soap and other small items. (Courtesy—*Woman's Day*.)

SCHUYLER SKUNK: Another small stool that would be a lot of fun for a younger brother or sister.

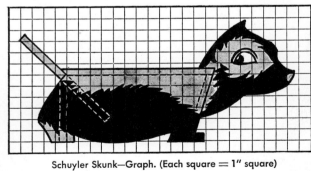

Schuyler Skunk—Graph. (Each square = 1" square)

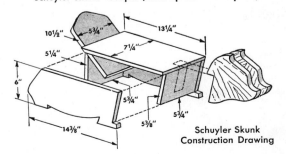

10$\frac{1}{2}$"   5$\frac{3}{4}$"   13$\frac{1}{4}$"

7$\frac{1}{4}$"

5$\frac{1}{4}$"

6"

5$\frac{3}{4}$"

14$\frac{3}{8}$"   5$\frac{3}{8}$"   5$\frac{3}{4}$"

Schuyler Skunk
Construction Drawing

199

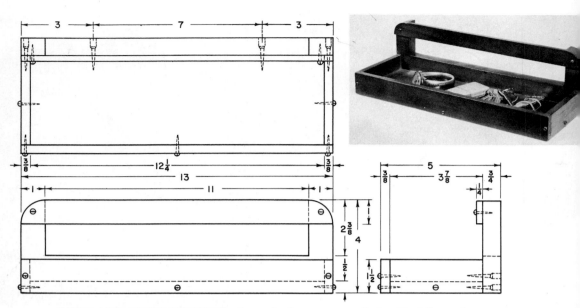

ODDS-AND-ENDS HOLDER: A good place to put all the "junk" you have in your pockets. You can fasten the holder to the wall or place it on a chest or dresser.

HANG-UP RACK: Just the rack for your room for your clothes, sports equipment or anything else you want to hang up.

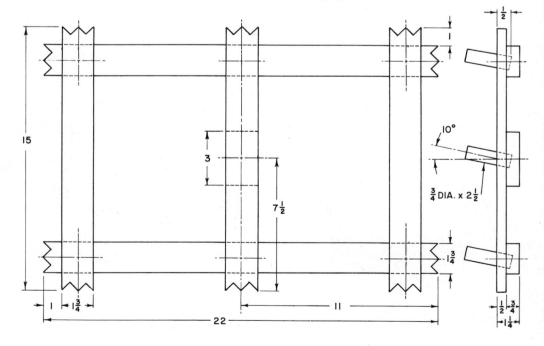

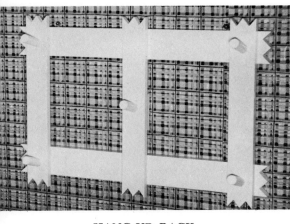

HANG-UP RACK

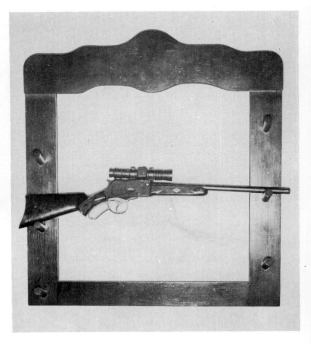

GUN RACK

GUN RACK: A very simple gun rack that will hold real or toy guns.

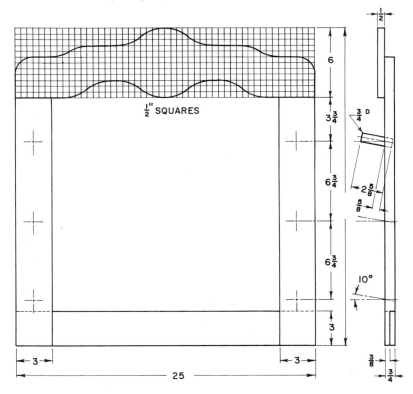

$\frac{1}{2}''$ SQUARES

Scot

FINISH THIS SCOTTY BY PAINTING ALL BLACK EXCEPT FOR THE EYES WHICH ARE WHITE SPOTS. DO NOT SAND-PAPER TO SMOOTH, LEAVE ANGLES SHARP TO GIVE A BETTER EFFECT.

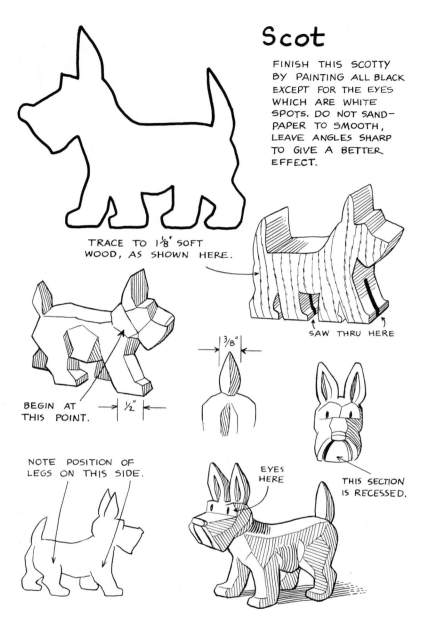

TRACE TO 1⅛" SOFT WOOD, AS SHOWN HERE.

SAW THRU HERE

BEGIN AT THIS POINT.

½"

⅜"

THIS SECTION IS RECESSED.

NOTE POSITION OF LEGS ON THIS SIDE.

EYES HERE

SCOT: A good whittling project for beginners.

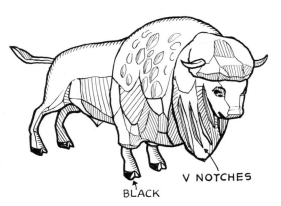

BLACK   V NOTCHES

ROAMING THE PRAIRIES IN COUNTLESS NUMBERS THE BUFFALO PROVIDED THE INDIANS WITH FOOD, CLOTHING AND SHELTER. NOW THE BUFFALO ARE GONE BUT IT IS EASY TO MAKE YOUR OWN. THE BLOCK SIZE WILL BE 1½" THICK - 3½" HIGH - 4½" WIDE, WITH GRAIN RUNNING VERTICAL. TRACE PATTERN ON TO BLOCK. SAW BETWEEN LEGS (to save whittling) AND DRILL HOLES FOR TAIL AND HORNS. START WHITTLING ON OUTSIDE SHOULDERS AS THIS IS THE WIDEST PORTION - FOLLOW THE DIFFERENT SKETCHES AND PROCEED TO FORM THE REST OF THE BUFFALO. FINISH WITH DARK BROWN STAIN - BUT DO NOT PAINT THE HORNS. ADD THE EYES AND NOSTRILS WITH BLACK INK.

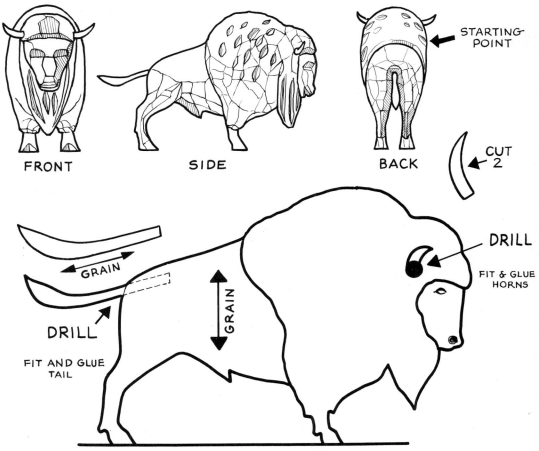

FRONT   SIDE   BACK

STARTING POINT

CUT 2

DRILL

FIT & GLUE HORNS

GRAIN

GRAIN

DRILL

FIT AND GLUE TAIL

BUFFALO: This will require more patience to complete.

203

CARVED CUTTING BOARD: Make this board of a good hardwood. It will add something special to your mother's kitchen. (Reprinted by permission of *Woman's Day* Magazine, September, 1954.)

KNIFE AND FORK SALAD SERVER: Should be made of walnut, mahogany or white wood. The long bowl to go with these is shown next. (Reprinted by permission of *Woman's Day* Magazine, September, 1954.)

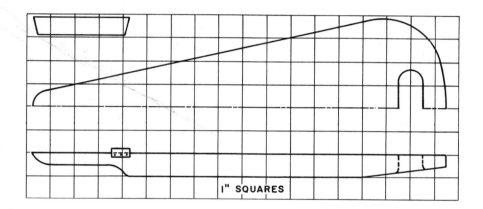

1" SQUARES

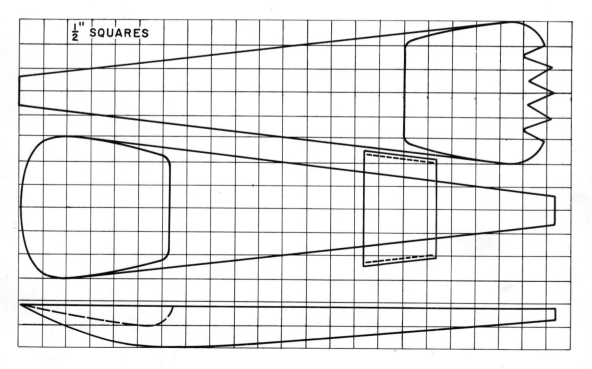

½" SQUARES

LONG BOWL: A beautiful decoration for a table. It can be used for fruit, flowers or salad. (Reprinted by permission of *Woman's Day* Magazine, September, 1954.)

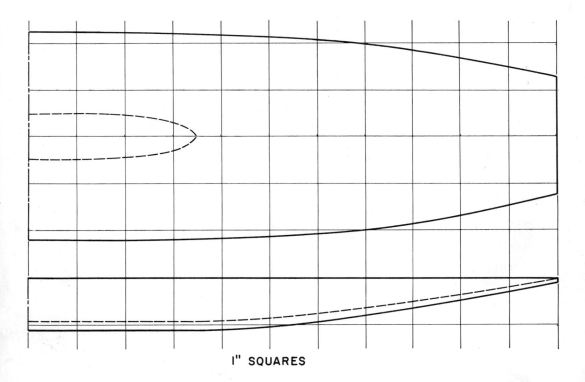

I" SQUARES

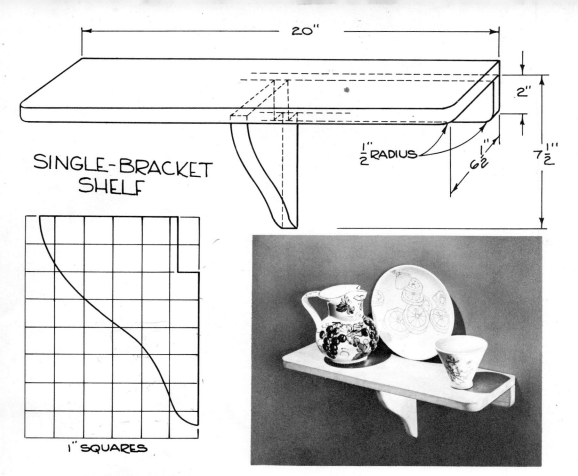

SINGLE-BRACKET SHELF

20"

2"

½" RADIUS

6½"

7½"

1" SQUARES

SINGLE-BRACKET SHELF: You can use this is your room for your radio, clock or any other small accessories. (Courtesy—*Woman's Day.*)

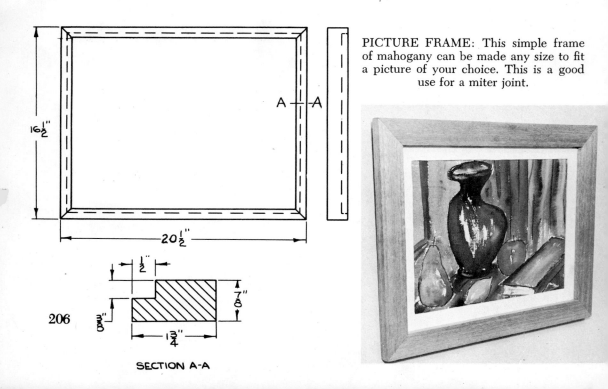

PICTURE FRAME: This simple frame of mahogany can be made any size to fit a picture of your choice. This is a good use for a miter joint.

16½"

A — A

20½"

½"

⅞"

¾"

1¾"

206

SECTION A-A

INDEX